Shore to Summit

F
FRANCES LINCOLN LIMITED
PUBLISHERS

SHORE TO SUMMIT

A PHOTOGRAPHIC GUIDE TO THE GEOLOGY
OF BRITAIN AND IRELAND

FRAN HALSALL

Frances Lincoln Ltd
74–77 White Lion Street
London N1 9PF
www.franceslincoln.com

A catalogue record for this book is available from the British Library.

ISBN 978-0-7112-3348-5

Printed in China

9 8 7 6 5 4 3 2 1

Half title page The high cliffs of the Trotternish Peninsula on the Isle of Skye provide excellent views across the sea towards the Torridon hills of north-west Scotland, which date from the Precambrian and are among the oldest sedimentary deposits in the British Isles. The pink half-light before sunrise reflects off the Sound of Raasay's waters.

Title page Sheer Carboniferous limestone cliffs fringe Flimston Bay near Merrion in Pembrokeshire, a location famous for the two sea stack that are home to a noisy seabird colony. Locally these rocks are known as the Elegug Stacks, after the Welsh word for guillemot.

Above Borthwen is a sheltered bay at Rhoscolyn on Anglesey's west coast, with views across Caenarfon Bay to the hazy peaks of the Lleyn Peninsula. Jagged metamorphic rocks protude from the mirror-still waters, a scene contrasting with the huge geological upheaval that took place here during the Precambrian.

Contents

Foreword   6

Geological Timescale   7

Introduction   9

Rocks in Motion   15

Plate Boundaries   16

Fold Types   17

Timeline   18

Photographs   20

Entering the Anthropocene?   184

Further Reading & Useful Websites   186

Glossary   187

Rock Data   189

Photographic Information   191

Foreword

First and foremost I am an artist, not a geologist, and this book is written in that spirit. When I began documenting the landscape many years ago, my initial motivation was the desire to create beautiful images. However, this rapidly evolved into an aim to depict natural processes as accurately as possible, and it soon became apparent that my geological knowledge was somewhat lacking. While it can be argued that landscape photography is primarily concerned with aesthetics, this is to dismiss its value as an aid to environmental interpretation. This can be achieved only if the photographer understands the nature of the subject. With this in mind, I started to delve deeper into the world's physical origins and came to realise that much of the information on the matter is either oversimplified or else presented in language that is not intended for the average reader, including myself. Then there is the fact that my inner visual critic was underwhelmed by much of the accompanying imagery, which failed to capture the drama of certain landforms and reduced rocks to flat-looking, grey masses. This failed to reflect my experience of rocks showing a range of colours, both subtle and vibrant, and being so exceptionally tactile that touching them is often irresistible.

These observations set in motion a series of thoughts about the kind of book I would have liked to have had at my fingertips from the outset: a volume that celebrated and explained the diversity of Britain and Ireland's geological heritage without skimming past the difficult topics, but that was not so weighed-down with detail that the bigger picture became obscured. As such, this is essentially the story of a hundred locations in context with major events in the Earth's history, and should be taken as a starting point for learning about the landscape. It is almost exclusively concerned with surface geology, the bits that can actually be seen, and the processes that have shaped them. Locations were chosen owing to their prominence within the landscape, both in a physical and historical (in a social sense) context, and their ability to demonstrate certain concepts.

A better grasp of geology has had a transformative effect on my responses to the wider landscape. Far from explaining away the strange power that rocks hold over my imagination, the more I know the more remarkable they become. My hope is that I can impart some of the wonder and demonstrate that, although geology is a technically demanding subject, it affects every aspect of life on this planet. To understand the origins of rocks is not only to appreciate where we have come from but also where we are heading.

Geological Timescale

Eon	Era	Period	Epoch	
			Holocene	11.7 ka
		Quaternary	Pleistocene	2.6 Ma
		Neogene	Pliocene	5.3 Ma
	Cainozoic		Miocene	23 Ma
			Oligocene	34 Ma
		Palaeogene	Eocene	56 Ma
			Paleocene	66 Ma
		Cretaceous	Upper	101 Ma
			Lower	145 Ma
			Upper	164 Ma
	Mesozoic	Jurassic	Middle	174 Ma
			Lower	201 Ma
			Upper	235 Ma
		Triassic	Middle	247 Ma
			Lower	253 Ma
			Lopingian	260 Ma
		Permian	Guadalupian	272 Ma
Phanerozoic			Cisuralian	299 Ma
			Pennsylvanian Upper	307 Ma
			Pennsylvanian Middle	315 Ma
	Paleozoic (Upper)	Carboniferous	Pennsylvanian Lower	323 Ma
			Mississippian Upper	331 Ma
			Mississippian Middle	347 Ma
			Mississippian Lower	359 Ma
			Upper	383 Ma
		Devonian	Middle	393 Ma
			Lower	419 Ma
			Pridoli	423 Ma
		Silurian	Ludlow	427 Ma
			Wenlock	433 Ma
	Paleozoic (Lower)		Llandovery	443 Ma
			Upper	458 Ma
		Ordovician	Middle	470 Ma
			Lower	485 Ma
			Furongian	497 Ma
		Cambrian	Series 3	509 Ma
			Series 2	521 Ma
			Terreneuvian	541 Ma
			Ediacaran	635 Ma
		Neoproterozoic	Cyrogenian	850 Ma
			Tonian	1000 Ma
			Stenian	1200 Ma
	Proterozoic	Mesoproterozoic	Ectasian	1400 Ma
			Calymmian	1600 Ma
Precambrian			Statherian	1800 Ma
		Paleoproterozoic	Orosirian	2050 Ma
			Rhyacian	2300 Ma
			Siderian	2500 Ma
		Neoarchean		2800 Ma
	Archean	Mesoarchean		3200 Ma
		Paleoarchean		3600 Ma
		Eoarchean		4000 Ma
	Hadean		Earth formed - 4600 Ma	

From the 2012 International Chronostratigraphic Chart

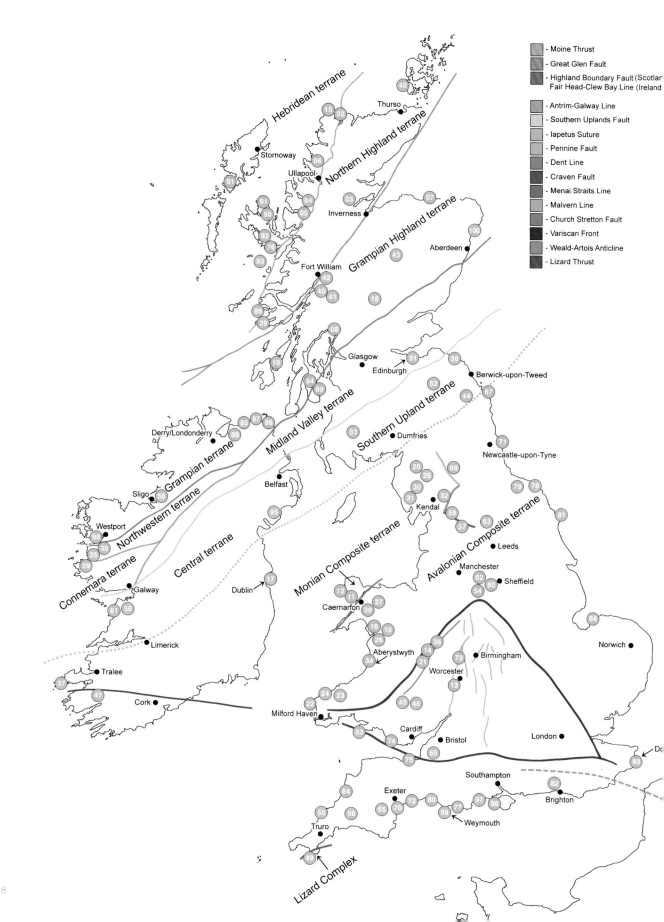

Moine Thrust

Great Glen Fault

Highland Boundary Fault (Scotland)
Fair Head-Clew Bay Line (Ireland)

Antrim-Galway Line

Southern Uplands Fault

Iapetus Suture

Pennine Fault

Dent Line

Craven Fault

Menai Straits Line

Malvern Line

Church Stretton Fault

Variscan Front

Weald-Artois Anticline

Lizard Thrust

Hebridean terrane

Northern Highland terrane

Grampian Highland terrane

Southern Upland terrane

Midland Valley terrane

Grampian terrane

Northwestern terrane

Central terrane

Connemara terrane

Monian Composite terrane

Avalonian Composite terrane

Lizard Complex

Thurso

Stornoway

Ullapool

Inverness

Aberdeen

Fort William

Glasgow

Edinburgh

Berwick-upon-Tweed

Derry/Londonderry

Dumfries

Newcastle-upon-Tyne

Belfast

Sligo

Westport

Kendal

Leeds

Manchester

Sheffield

Galway

Dublin

Caernarfon

Norwich

Limerick

Aberystwyth

Birmingham

Tralee

Worcester

Cork

Milford Haven

Cardiff

Bristol

London

Southampton

Truro

Exeter

Weymouth

Brighton

Introduction

Although Britain and Ireland are not large countries, for their size they encompass more geological variety than practically any other comparable area in the world. Rocks from nearly every stage of the Earth's history are represented on these islands, either at or close to the surface, helping to explain why the forefathers of geological science found so much evidence here to corroborate their theories. This is why many of the greatest advances in the discipline began in the British Isles and why so many geological periods are associated with these islands through their names, such as the Devonian (referring to the Old Red Sandstone of Devon), the Ordovician and the Silurian (named after ancient Celtic tribes), and the Cambrian (after Cambria, the Latinised name for Wales).

This broad range of rocks is partly due to the different positions that the British and Irish landmasses have occupied throughout their development. Although we currently enjoy a temperate climate, in the past conditions have ranged from sub-tropical oceans to frozen expanses, and from arid deserts to lush rainforest. Each phase created characteristic rock types and associated geomorphology (i.e. the shape of land). This geodiversity is responsible for the many different faces of the British landscape, albeit with a lot of help from humans who have tamed all but the most impractical and inaccessible places. Rocks are the framework that not only establish physical appearance but also affect the habitat by determining the soil, its fertility and its drainage, and therefore where and how we live.

Today, Britain and Ireland are located a comfortable distance away from the edge of the Eurasian Plate, which is one of the many mobile plates that together make up the globe's surface, and both are undergoing a quiet phase geologically. The British Isles no longer experiences volcanic activity and any earthquakes are minor and infrequent events. However, there are many visible reminders of a more turbulent geological past. In peaceful parts of the planet the major rock forming process is sedimentary deposition, by which eroded particles from existing rocks are laid down in layers that solidify (lithify) over many millions of years (Ma) under the weight of accumulating particles above. These layers, or strata, are affected by earth movements and can be fractured and faulted, folded and uplifted.

At active tectonic plate boundaries, magma from within the Earth's molten mantle is erupted as lava, ash and other ejecta from volcanoes, and together these are classed as extrusive igneous rocks. However, not all igneous rocks are produced in such a dramatic way, as they are also formed intrusively in underground magma chambers that solidify before they reach the surface. An additional process occurs at plate margins when the Earth's crust is put under huge pressures and becomes superheated, leading to deformation of rocks. This is known as metamorphism and it transforms both sedimentary and igneous rocks into new forms with different internal structures. Each original rock type, known as the protolith,

Portknockie, Moray, banded quartzite
Precambrian/Cambrian boundary

Iron oxide originally deposited parallel to horizontal quartzite beds is now contorted into swirling bands, indicating the extent of the deformation in these metamorphosed coastal rocks (area shown approximately 70cm high).

Gable Beck, Wasdale, pink granite
Ordovician

Coarse-textured granite resists erosion well, but even this rock can be worn smooth by a mountain stream over the course of many thousands of years (area shown approximately 1.2m high).

St David's Head, Pembrokeshire, oxidised gabbro
Ordovician

Gabbro is often a dark-coloured rock, although in this instance it is a rusty-orange colour due to the high iron content being oxidised on exposure to the air in this coastal location (area shown approximately 30cm high).

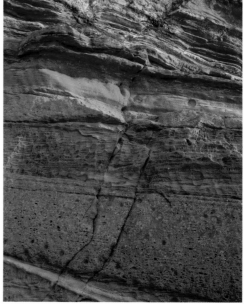

Pease Bay, Berwickshire, Old Red Sandstone
Devonian

These iron-pigmented sea cliffs show cross-bedding, an inclined sedimentary structure formed as the layers were deposited rather than by subsequent Earth movements. This occurs in both river (fluvial) and windblown (aeolian) deposits (area shown approximately 2.5m high).

has its own associated metamorphic varieties and these alter according to the amount of exposure to heat and pressure. They can be arranged on a sliding scale: for example, sedimentary shale becomes metamorphic slate, which can then be further metamorphosed into phyllite, which is itself an intermediate stage on the way to becoming a micaceous schist.

Our planet is a dynamic place, but only by taking the long view can the cyclical processes of erosion and renewal that are at the heart of it all be fully appreciated. There is nothing new under the sun as all created matter borrows its constituent elements from the planet's finite supply. Younger rocks are made from older ones, be they igneous, sedimentary or metamorphic. They all have the potential to be broken down over time through erosion, or changed by temperature and pressure. It is all part of the great recycling. We have become a part of this process as we accelerate the rate of erosion through tree clearance and agriculture – which destabilise topsoil – quarrying and mineral extraction, peat-bog cutting, and through overused footpaths that cause ugly scars across some of our best-loved landscapes. There is also anthropogenically accelerated climate change to consider, and the potential this has to reshape radically our planet's geography and atmosphere, two systems that are inextricably linked.

There is evidence to suggest that ancient Egyptian and Chinese philosophers were interested in the natural origins of the Earth as long as 4,000 years ago. The ancient Greeks added much to the pool of knowledge regarding the planet's physical structure. Although they initially associated geological events with tales of gods and monsters, they increasingly moved towards logical interpretations of these myths in the search for underlying truths. Even so, we have always sought less prosaic explanations for the landscape's origins, and colourful legends abound as to why things look the way they do. Gods, the Devil and giants were often credited with the more unusual formations, while volcanoes became associated with fiery dragons, and earthquakes were attributed to restless monsters relegated to the underworld by supreme beings. Certain geomyths have been found to be at least partially accurate in their description of natural events, even if others are delightfully wide of the mark.

Some of these stories influence the names chosen for landforms and others recall cultural heroes, while many simply refer to physical attributes or the place they occupy in the human imagination. Whatever the case, what we call landforms reveals something about our historical relationship with our environment, confirming that these places 'belong' to us and are a part of our psyche. While some names and their associated folktales remain, many others have been obscured by time. In turn, references to rocks and landscape features have become a 'cornerstone' of our language, with similes such as 'solid as a rock', 'old as the hills', 'set in stone' and the 'lie of the land' all in regular usage.

Landscapes and landforms have long been the focus for social and spiritual customs, and our relationship with rock stretches back far into prehistory. As early humans moved out of Africa into the cooler climate of Europe, caves were a vital source of shelter and became part of our cultural development as we decorated the walls with paintings and carvings. We have progressed to our current level of relative sophistication in a comparatively short time. The development of stone tools is one of the defining moments of our evolution. The stone tools of East Africa are the oldest known, dating back over 2 Ma, the product of an ancient species called *Homo habilis*. There is some evidence that an older human ancestor, *Australopithecus afarensis*, may even have been using primitive stone tools more than 3 Ma.

The use of tools has allowed us to become the dominant species on the planet, overcoming our limitations in otherwise harsh environments. From those first stone tools, all human technology followed.

Around 800,000 years before the present (BP), long before modern humans evolved, the first representations of the interior world of mind began to appear in the form of sculpted stone. These were either petroglyphs cut into rock surfaces or small crudely carved statues, the earliest surviving of which – the Venus of Berekhat Ram – remains controversial, as although some maintain that it depicts a female 'mother goddess', this is not universally accepted. Other materials such as wood and bone were also used; however, it is stone art that has revealed most about the culture and the developing consciousness of early hominids. Stone is still the choice material for statuary and sculpture, partly because of its enduring presence but due also to its inherent visual and tactile appeal.

Some theorise that rocks became symbolic because of their ability to outlast the human timescale. Burial sites dating back 20,000–30,000 years indicate that there was an interest in fossils and minerals, and later stones themselves were used in the construction of monuments to the dead. This practice dates from around 10,000–6,000 BP (during the European Mesolithic), when humans were drifting away from a hunter-gatherer lifestyle towards agriculture and settled communities. This custom is still echoed in the use of headstones and other grander funerary monuments. Around 6,000–4,000 BP (during the European Neolithic), monuments became increasingly elaborate in their construction and began to be arranged into significant alignments such as the rows at Brittany's Carnac, or circles such as Wiltshire's Stonehenge. While the exact purpose of these monuments is unknown, the fact that they were exceptionally important is shown by the amount of effort that went into making them.

Today we see rocks through the prism of science and we may deem ourselves too rational to invest them with 'magical' significance. However, consider the urge to pick up and pocket an interesting pebble while out walking on a beach, or to run one's hand over a sculpture in spite of the 'do not touch' sign. Think also of rock-climbing and mounaineering, where the desire to pit one's wits against nature's challenges and to be 'on top of the world' can pose a real threat to life. A less thrill-seeking expression of this primal behaviour is the almost ritualistic thronging to scenic spots, some of which are so popular that on fine summer weekends they can seem as busy as the urban spaces from which we are escaping.

Part of the attraction of rocks is that we can experience them on a range of scales, from the intimate contemplation of the pebble in the palm of the hand, to the awe-inspiring vastness of mountain ranges and beyond to the entire planet itself. Bound up with their physicality are the strong emotions they inspire, and it is surprising how animated we can get about this cold, hard substance. There are famous landforms that are so loved that they have reached the status of national icons; and of equal importance are the local landmarks that remind us of our own geographical origin. They provide inspiration for artists, poets, writers and musicians, who embed them in our cultural landscape, further heightening their symbolic value.

The Burren, County Clare, limestone pavement
Carboniferous

Blackberry, common ivy and sticky bud all thrive within the
shallow calcareous (lime-rich) soil of a grike, the eroded channel
within a limestone pavement: these glacio-karst landforms,
shaped by ice and water, are widespread in central Ireland's
upland habitats (area shown approximately 60cm high).

Millook Haven, Cornwall, quartz in killas
Carboniferous

Killas is the local name for the slate/phyllite metamorphosed
sedimentary rock found throughout Cornwall and seen here on its
north-west coast: these rock beds fractured under massive stress,
allowing the gaps to be filled with quartz dissolved in solution, forming
crystals as the fluid evaporated (area shown approximately 50cm high).

Holy Island, Northumberland, dolerite
Permian

Although exceptionally hard, dolerite eventually yields
to the sea's abrasive force: despite harsh and salty
conditions, specialist organisms such as orange sea
lichen thrive, further attacking and weakening the rock's
surface (area shown approximately 80cm high).

**Littleham Cove, Devon,
radioactive ore in mudstone**
Permo-Triassic

The presence of a tiny uranium-vanadium nodule
embedded in coastal cliffs is revealed by the halo created
around it: the host rock's red colour is due to iron in its
oxidised form, while the pale green is from iron in its
reduced form (area shown approximately 20cm high).

Lyme Regis, Dorset, limestone
Jurassic

Fossilised Arietitid-type ammonites on the foreshore at low tide. Ammonites were once one of the most abundant sea creatures and are common fossils. Historically they were called serpentstones as they were taken for coiled-up petrified snakes (area shown approximately 30cm high).

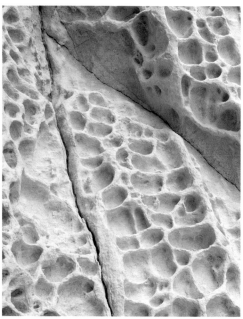

Elgol, Isle of Skye, sandstone
Jurassic

This pale sandstone is mainly quartz (silica) and where the mineral is at its densest concentration, the rock is more resistant to chemical weathering by the sea's salty spray, creating the peculiarly organic-looking honeycomb erosion pattern across the entire cliff face (area shown approximately 40cm high).

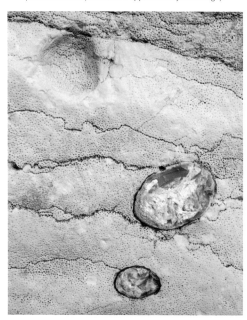

White Rocks Bay, County Antrim, flint in chalk
Cretaceous

Glassy flint nodules, formed out of silica from sea-sponge skeletons dissolved in oceanic waters, are common in chalk beds and became exposed owing to erosion. Chalk is created from the remains of microscopic hard-shelled organisms called coccolithophores (area shown approximately 20cm high).

**Cleiteadh nan Sgarbh, Arran,
quartz-porphyry and granite**
Palaeogene

A grey granite pebble has become lodged in quartz porphyry, and both rocks share an intrusive igneous origin. Cross-sections of large quartz crystals can be seen in the porphyry matrix where waves have polished the surface smooth (area shown approximately 30cm high).

Rocks in Motion

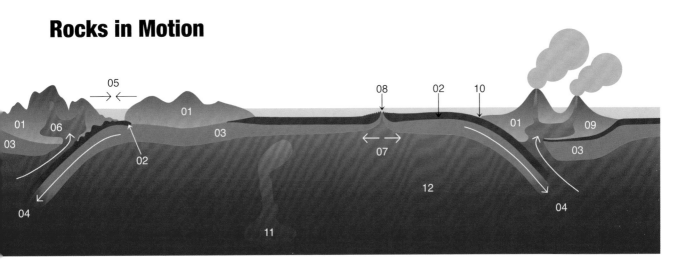

Earth's surface is made up of tectonic plates, which are composed of both continental [01] and oceanic crust [02]. These plates drift incrementally across the mantle [03], the upper reaches of which are composed of partially melted magma. Together these three elements are known as the lithosphere.

Where plates move towards each other (convergence), if at least one plate is composed of oceanic crust, then one plate is forced to pass underneath the other and the lower one descends into the mantle in a process known as subduction [04]. If both plates are composed of continental crust, they collide and are uplifted, creating fold mountain ranges. As continents are pulled towards each other it has the effect of shrinking the intervening ocean [05]. As the oceanic crust is squeezed, the seafloor is folded upwards, as are any overlying areas of continental crust creating mountain ranges that often feature magma chambers at their core, as the pressure and heat generated through subduction is enough to melt the rocks at the base of the fold belt [06].

On the opposite side of the plate from the subduction zone the plate margin shifts away from the neighbouring plate (divergence) and a gap opens up [07]. Magma from the mantle is forced upwards under huge pressure through this fissure creating a spreading ridge where new crust forms to fill the gap. When this happens on land, rift volcanoes are the result; however, if it occurs on the seafloor it creates a mid-ocean ridge with an accompanying trench [08]. In the former case the continent grows and in the latter case the ocean expands.

The process of convergence and divergence can be likened to a conveyor belt, as subduction at one boundary is balanced out by continental/sea-floor spread at the other, keeping the total surface of the globe in balance. Some of the most active geological processes are to be found in subduction zones, the most violent expressions of which are earthquakes and volcanoes.

A volcanic arc, so named because the chain is arranged in a crescent shape, occurs where an oceanic plate is subducted underneath another plate. An oceanic arc [09] is a series of island volcanoes frequently aligned in parallel to an ocean trench [10], which itself is created as the oceanic plate descends into the mantle beneath another oceanic plate. A continental volcanic arc is the equivalent on land, which forms when oceanic crust subducts beneath continental crust.

A hotspot [11] is a plume of exceptionally hot magma from the upper mantle's lower section, known as the asthenosphere [12], which can occur in conjunction with plate margins or independently as shown. The hot spot is in a fixed position but as plates pass overhead it has the potential to punch through and create a series of volcanoes.

Plate Boundaries

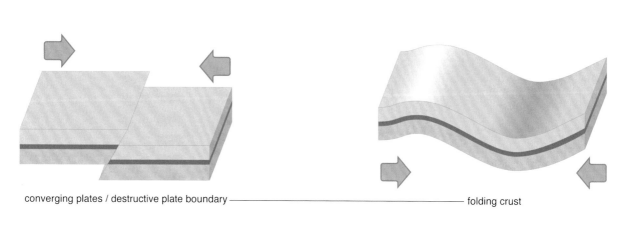

converging plates / destructive plate boundary ——————————————— folding crust

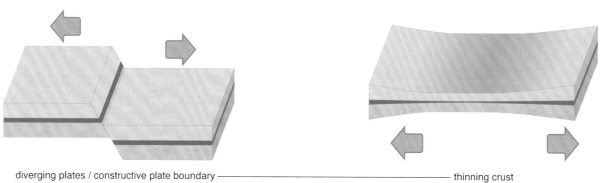

diverging plates / constructive plate boundary ——————————————— thinning crust

transform fault / conservative plate boundary —————————————— shearing crust

Fold Types

monoclinal folding

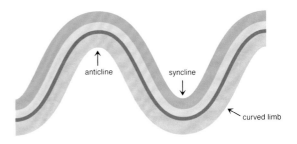

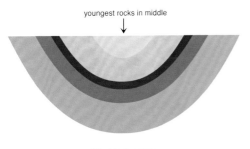

filled in syncline

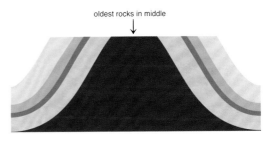

eroded anticline

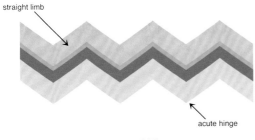

chevron folding

overfolding

13,800 Ma – The 'Big Bang' starts the Universe

4,600 Ma – Our Sun, and the Solar System form

3,800 Ma – Chemical reactions in water create the first organic molecules

2,400 Ma – Earth's 1st Ice Age, which lasts 300 million years

2,000 Ma – Eucaryotes (single-celled organisms containing a nucleus) evolve

4,000 Ma – Volcanic activity forms what are now the oldest rocks on Earth

3,500 Ma – Primitive bacteria evolve from amino acids

PRECAMBRIAN

Britain and Ireland are dominated by shallow seas and coral reefs

420 Ma – The first vascular plants evolve

450–445 Ma – The Ordovician–Silurian extinction event

SILURIAN

420 Ma – The first sharks evolve

410 Ma – Insects resembling mayflies suggest first forays into flight

DEVONIAN

400 Ma – Primitive amphibians evolve

375 Ma – A 2nd major extiction kills of 50% of life over 20 million years

360 Ma – Gymnosperms (seed-bearing plants) begin colonising Earth

The spread of land plants increases oxygen levels, initiating 4th major Ice Age

Britain and Ireland are part of a semi-arid landmass, criss-crossed with meandering river systems

Rising warm seas teaming with life inundate Britain and Ireland

Britain and Ireland remain warm and tropical, with shallow seas, lagoons and river systems

JURASSIC

145 Ma – Pangaea begins to break up

155 Ma – Archaeopteryx appears

CRETACEOUS

130 Ma – Flowering plants proliferate

66 Ma – 5th major extinction wipes out dinosaurs and 75% of all other species

60 Ma – first primate and rodents

PALAE

Britain and Ireland's climate cools as it moves northwards and most of the country is land fringed by shallow seas

2.4 Ma – First members of our genus, *Homo*, found in fossil record

QUAR

600,000 years – *Homo heidelbergensis*, the likely direct ancestor of both *Homo neanderthalensis* and *Homo sapiens*, evolves. Groups of this species migrate northwards and reach Britain and Ireland

250,000 years – *Homo sapiens* evolves in Africa

100,000 years – *Homo sapiens* begins to spread out of Africa and across the globe

10,000 years – glacia period ends, and humans return northwards

850–635 Ma – Earth's 2nd Ice Age

Multicellular life begins to thrive

580 Ma – Life starts to diversify rapidly

530 Ma – The 'Cambrian Explosion'

Britain and Ireland lie well into the Southern hemisphere

First signs of life moving out of the sea

CAMBRIAN

525 Ma – First vertebrates with true bones

450 Ma – Invertebrates venture out of the sea

460 Ma – Tectonic movement takes the Gondwana supercontinent south – 3rd major Ice Age

470 Ma – The first land plants evolve

ORDOVICIAN

Britain and Ireland lie under shallow seas

Britain and Ireland are covered first by seas, and later by coal swamps as the sea level drops

...40 Ma – the first ...olely terrestrial ...nimals evolve

CARBONIFEROUS

300 Ma – the supercontinent Pangaea is created

280 Ma – earliest beetles evolve

Britain and Ireland are dominated by desert, with a shallow, salty sea

265 Ma – Ammonites diversify, and the first reptiles evolve

PERMIAN

Britain and Ireland are desert plains intersected by river systems

225 Ma – first dinosaurs

251 Ma – Earth's third and most signicant extinction occurs. 75% of terrestrial life and 95% of marine life dies.

TRIASSIC

220 Ma – gymnosperm forests, including conifers, cycads and ginkgoes dominate Earth's vegetation

205 Ma – 4th major extinction. 50% of life is eliminated

Britain and Ireland's woodlands take on a familiar look with boradleaved oak and beech, but giant redwoods and palms are also part of the landscape

Britain and Ireland's climate cools as it moves northwards and most of the country is land fringed by shallow seas

...GENE

34–28 Ma – North Sea forms

...40 Ma – first ...butterflies and moths

7 Ma – Last common ancestor of humans and chimpanzees

4 Ma – *Australopithecus* evolves in Africa

15 Ma – Grasslands spread far and wide as climate cools

NEOGENE

2.6 Ma – 5th major Ice Age begins

...7 Ma – Extinction of Austrolopithecus

1.5 Ma – Early humans may have begun using fire

...ENARY

...000 years – ...griculture begins in ...esopotamia

6,000 years – Neolithic farmers begin the deforestation of Britain and Ireland

5,000 years – the development of writing

1 Taigh Bhuirgh and Toe Head, Isle of Harris, Outer Hebrides

The gneisses of north-west Scotland, including those found in the western Hebrides, are the oldest in the British Isles. These outcrops of Lewisian gneiss (after Harris's neighbour the Isle of Lewis) have been dated to 3,000 Ma. making them part of the Precambrian Eon. An eon is the highest rank when classifying geological time, which is then sub-divided into eras, periods, epochs and ages. Unusually, the Precambrian is a supereon consisting of three eons: the Hadean (after Hades, the Ancient Greek underworld), the Archean (Greek for 'beginning') and the Proterozoic (Greek for 'earlier life'). This supereon encompasses an immense expanse of time from the formation of the Earth at 4,600 Ma to the start of the current Phanaerozoic Eon at 541 Ma. Metamorphic gneiss was once volcanic material erupted during the Archean Eon (4,000–2,500 Ma) and then buried as the first tectonic cycle began and continental plates started to shift across the globe's surface. At the end of the Archean these igneous rocks were dragged down into a subduction zone on a destructive plate boundary and were subjected to great heat and pressure, transforming them into gneisses.

The Hebridean terrane is geologically distinct and separated from the rest of Scotland by the Moine Thrust belt (see Beinn Eighe, page 24). The same type of rocks can be identified in eastern Canada and in Greenland, which confirms that they were once connected as part of the ancient continent of Laurentia. Although Archean rocks form the basement of all continents, they are seen only at the surface where earth movements or erosion have revealed them. Scottish gneiss scenery is typified by long and rounded hills such as Ceapabhal, on the Toe Head peninsula, which have been worn smooth by passing ice.

With distant age comes a certain lack of clarity, and the bigger picture in the Precambrian is less well understood than in later periods. This is partly due to the shortage of fossils as the few organisms existing at this stage were soft-bodied and left little or no trace. Consequently it was long thought that the Precambrian was azoic or 'without life'. But rocks showing evidence of microbial life have been identified dating back around 3,500 Ma and, towards the eon's end in the Ediacaran Period (635–541 Ma), the oldest remains of multicellular organisms are found.

PRECAMBRIAN
4,600–541 Ma

2 Rubha na Griosaich, Durness, Sutherland

Powerful forces caused these salmon pink gneiss cliffs at Rubha na Griosaich – or Point of the Embers – on Scotland's north-west coast to be tilted upright, and they perfectly illustrate the impact of colliding continents. The vertical alignment is easily seen because of well defined cracks, most probably caused by shrinkage along the joints in between the rock layers as they cooled. The banding evident within gneissic rocks is created when the different constituent minerals are resorted into distinct layers as they are transformed from the original rock (protolith). This foliation is often a prominent and identifying feature of gneiss and other metamorphic rocks such as schist.

Although the Atlantic Ocean separates them today, both Scotland and the north-western part of Ireland, along with North America and Newfoundland, were once part of the same continent, Laurentia. At this time Laurentia lay approximately 20° south of the equator while England, Wales and south-eastern Ireland, which formed separately on the northern edge of the Gondwana supercontinent, were at 60° south and close to the Antarctic Circle. Laurentia too was once part of Gondwana, but it broke away and drifted northwards towards the equator, opening up the Iapetus Ocean in its wake, which at its greatest extent stretched for 7,000km between the two landmasses. This means that the British Isles are today closer to North America than Scotland and the north-western part of Ireland were to England, Wales and south-eastern Ireland during the Precambrian, as North America is now only 3,000km across the Atlantic from Ireland's west coast. This initial geographical isolation goes some way to explaining the notable differences between the landscapes of the northern and southern fragments that come together to form the British Isles.

3 Ben Wyvis, near Dingwall, Highland

PRECAMBRIAN
4,600–541 Ma

The Moinian rocks comprising the Northern Highland terrane are bordered by the Moine Thrust (see page 24) to the north-west and the Great Glen Fault to the south-east, and were the last area of the Scottish Highlands to be surveyed in detail. This sequence, also known as the Moine Supergroup, dates from the Proterozoic Eon and is dominated by metamorphic schists and some slices of gneiss. These were originally sandstones (from quartz-rich sand) and fine-grained shales (mud with clay minerals and sand) deposited in fairly shallow seas in the early-Neoproterozoic Era (Tonian Period 1,000–850 Ma) that then underwent three separate episodes of intense metamorphism and drastic folding during the mid-Neoproterozoic Era (Cryogenian Period 850–635 Ma) and in the Ordovician (485–443 Ma) and Silurian (443–419 Ma) periods. The resultant scenery includes high and bulky mountains blunted by the passage of recurring ice-sheets. Ben Wyvis, a 5km ridge running north-south, reaches 1,046m above sea level and has little in the way of distinguishing features. It is composed of pelitic gneiss, an attribution denoting its origin as a fine-grained sedimentary rock.

The origin of Ben Wyvis' name is not certain, although some think it is derived from 'Uabhis' or 'Futhas', both of which can be interpreted as meaning 'terror'. It is unclear whether this is a reference to the mountain's presence or some unpleasant historical event. The name of the range's highest top is easily explained, as Glas Leathad Mór translates as 'big green slope', almost certainly a reference to the woolly fringe-moss extensively colonising the summit plateau. In fact, the habitat on Ben Wyvis is known to support the largest single tract of this mat-forming moss in Britain, which thrives on the acidic soil derived from the eroding silica-rich bedrock.

The mountain is at the northern extent of historical Clan Munro lands. The Munro name is synonymous with Scotland's tallest peaks – those that reach over 3,000ft (914m) high – as it was the 4th Baronet, Sir Hugh, who first assembled the list. There are 283 mountains qualifying as 'Munros' and when arranged in descending height order Ben Wyvis is number 85 on the list. Sir Hugh never ascended all those listed, but in his attempts to do so he initiated the pastime known as 'Munro bagging'.

4 Beinn Eighe, Glen Torridon, Highland

The Torridon mountains are formed from huge terraces of sandstone dating from around 800 Ma, and Torridonian rocks comprise the bulk of the eastern Hebridean terrane. They were laid down when broad rivers brought sediments and gravel from the mountains of what is now Greenland, which then settled in lakes across an arid landscape, a process known as alluvial deposition. The climate of the time can be determined from the sandstone's characteristic red-purple hue, which is caused by iron rusting within the rocks when exposed to the air. Many of the Earth's significant iron ore deposits are from the oldest sedimentary rocks, as during the Precambrian great quantities of the element were to be found dissolved in seawater, making the early oceans bright green. This iron bonded with oxygen to form the minerals magnetite and haematite, laid down as part of banded ironstone formations.

Scotland's north-west is separated from the rest of the Highlands by the Moine Thrust, a major fault running along the eastern perimeter of the Torridonian deposits. It was created during continental collision occurring 400 million years after these sandstones were laid down. The impact forced older Moine metasediments (metamorphosed sediments) and Lewisian basement gneisses over the top of younger deposits, a fact that flies in the face of common sense and the 'Law of Superposition', which states that sedimentary rocks run in sequence from the oldest at the bottom to the youngest on top. This law holds throughout many sedimentary units but thrust belts are notorious for complicating the chronological picture.

Unlike the other Torridon peaks, Beinn Eighe's highest reaches are composed of light-coloured quartzite, a metamorphosed form of sandstone dating from the dawn of the Cambrian period. This pale rock was once a sandy beach of pure quartz grains that developed along the shore of the growing Iapetus Ocean. The hard-wearing quartzite creates a serrated ridge, the visual impact of which is acknowledged in the name that translates as 'File Mountain'. The rock also forms scree slopes of loose stone, and from the ground this jumble of reflective fragments can easily be mistaken for a light dusting of snow.

5 Liathach and Loch Bharranch, Glen Torridon, Highland

Liathach is separated from Beinn Eighe, the foot of which is seen here, by Coire Dubh Mor, and at 1,055m is higher still. Along with Beinn Eighe, Liathach – or 'the grey one' – looms large above the eastern approach to Glen Torridon. Viewed from the boggy margins of Loch Bharranch, it is shaped like a dome with stepped edges formed from alternating sandstone and shale terraces arranged on a monumental scale. Unlike the rest of the Scottish Highlands, the Torridonian rocks have been little altered since being laid down and this provides a clue as to how the landscape may have looked before Earth-shaping events swept through the rest of Scotland.

Where Liathach ends Loch Torridon begins, and is filled by water running off the mountains before eventually feeding into the Atlantic Ocean. The further back in time we reach, the less we know: however, recent discoveries in rocks around the loch have offered an insight into the story of early life. Fossils from rocks formed on a lakebed 1,000 Ma record the earliest known multicellular algae. These basic organisms had the cellular structures necessary for photosynthesis, meaning they were among the first organisms to use the Sun's energy to draw carbon dioxide from the atmosphere as an energy source. Organisms like these released oxygen into the atmosphere as a by-product, initiating the most dramatic change in the atmosphere life on Earth has ever seen, and creating an environment more suited to the evolution of complex life. Thus, we can attribute our own existence to the development of these algae.

6 Stac Pollaidh and Ben More Coigach, Assynt-Coigach, Sutherland

The Assynt-Coigach area is famous for its numerous Torridonian sandstone peaks soaring high above a Lewisian gneiss basement of small rolling hills partially submerged under lochs, which is otherwise known as a 'knock and lochan' style landscape (from *cnoc*, meaning 'knoll'). Stac Pollaidh (612m), an inselberg, or island mountain, is bounded by water on most sides, including Loch Lurgainn to the south, which lies at the foot of Ben More Coigach. This location marks a missing layer of time, where rocks from an intervening phase have completely eroded away prior to the formation of today's mountains. A gap in the otherwise continuous deposition of sediments is known as an unconformity, and here the absent rocks represent a time interval of over 2,000 million years. The unconformity between the gneiss and sandstone is the earliest in the British Isles.

The summit geology on Stac Pollaidh is severely weathered, compared with neighbouring mountains, and features impressive pinnacles and plunging gullies. The rocks exhibit a distinctive raised surface pattern and the complexity of this, along with other eroded features, suggest that the peak was not scoured and smoothed by ice during glaciations. These summit formations are readily identified and have names such as the 'Lobster's Claw' and the 'Madonna and Child'.

Stac Pollaidh, or 'Hill of the Peat Moss', is among the most accessible of the Assynt-Coigach peaks and, although far from the highest, is certainly one of the best known: and has unsurprisingly been Anglicised to 'Stack Polly', a phonetic interpretation of the original Gaelic. In spite of the peak's iconic status, in 2004 it was proposed as a site for a new radio transmitter. Public outcry followed, the company concerned having seriously underestimated the strength of local people's attachment to this memorable little mountain. Eventually the transmitter was located elsewhere but the incident was held up as an example of 'outsider' insensitivity to the landscape's cultural importance to the people living there.

7 Bow Fiddle Rock, Portknockie, Moray

Shaped like a bow or an elephant, depending on your point of view, Bow Fiddle Rock is a distinctive arch at Portknockie on the Moray Firth. What remains of the arch is formed from quartzite as the softer schist has eroded away. The rocks forming this stretch of Scotland's east coast were originally beds of limestone and sandstone deposited in the shallow sea at Laurentia's margins around 650 Ma during the Cryogenian Period (850–635 Ma). This was a climatically harsh time of retreating and advancing ice sheets, possibly extending from both poles as far as the equator, giving rise to the nickname 'Snowball Earth'. The 'Cryo' designation comes from the Greek *kryos*, meaning icy cold.

These sediments became metamorphosed into schist and quartzite during a sequence of events initiated by continental collision beginning around 200 million years after these beds were originally laid down during the Silurian period (443–419 Ma). Under sideways pressure the land within the impact zone was folded upwards, an episode known as the Caledonian Orogeny, eventually creating a mountain range as high as the Himalayas. These Caledonian Mountains were part of a belt that extended across Britain and Ireland, and on into Greenland and Scandinavia. This episode was responsible for scooping Portknockie's rocks off the seafloor and pushing them onto the land, tilting them to a 45° angle in the process.

Together, these metasediments are referred to as Dalradian, after the historic Dál Riata Scottish region, and are confined to an area bounded by the Great Glen Fault to the north-west and the Highland Boundary Fault to the south-east. The Dalradian series spans the Precambrian/Cambrian boundary and is a complicated set of rocks to read owing to the radical reconfigurations sustained during the Caledonian Orogeny.

8 The Cobbler, Arrochar, Argyll and Bute

The Cobbler, otherwise known as Ben Arthur, is named after three distinct summits said to resemble a shoemaker at work. Its shape is thought to be due to rock slope failure, a loss of integrity in a mountainside exacerbated by erosion, which leads to landslips ranging from localised events to full-on cataclysms. The Cobbler (884m) is one of the Arrochar Alps that are part of the Grampian Mountains, formed during the main Grampian phase of the Caledonian Orogeny. As Beinn Ìme, the highest in the Arrochar group, is only 1,011m, the Alpine designation seems overblown (as a comparison, the highest mountain in the European Alps is Mont Blanc, at 4,810m); however, it actually refers to the original stature of the Caledonian chain to which they belong.

Metamorphosis of the original marine sediments transformed the rocks into mica-schist, which means they must have been buried at about 20km below the crust surface, heated to between 500–1,000°C and put under pressures 20,000 times that of normal atmosphere. The presence of different minerals within the rocks can be used as a temperature gauge as each has their own preferred conditions in which to generate. Schist has a foliated structure and takes it name from the Greek for 'easily cleft', in recognition of the ease with which it can be split along the mineral plane.

The mountain gave its name to the Cobbler Club, which was an early climbing group founded in 1866 by Professor Ramsay of Glasgow University. The Arrochar area is easily accessible from Glasgow, making it the obvious playground for city-dwelling mountain enthusiasts. They would certainly have found much to challenge them here, mica-schist being treacherously slippery when wet. The mountain has a long tradition of testing the mettle of the local Clan Campbell's young men, as only those who could reach the top were permitted to become clan chief.

9 The Twelve Pins, Connemara, County Galway

The Twelve Pins are also called the Twelve Bens, Ben being the Anglicised version of Irish *beanna* or Scottish *beinn*, which sometimes becomes *binn* – hence 'pin'. These quartzite mountains, laid down over schist, epitomise the rugged character of Connemara on Ireland's western fringe. Most are between 600m and 700m, with Benbaun peaking at 729m, so the range is prominent above the low-lying coast. The quartzite recurs in the Maumturks range to the west, just visible here beyond Kylemore Lough.

During the most recent glacial period, almost all this landscape's soil was eroded away, leaving a harsh environment dominated by rock and clothed in peat bog formed over thousands of years from decomposing vegetation. As with the Scottish Highland interior this is not an easy place to live, especially because of climatic cooling since the European Iron Age (800 BC to AD 100). However, Connemara was once home to the Connache Mara, a branch of the Conmache tribe that ranged across the old Connacht Province and who gave their name to the region. 'Mara', meaning sea, demonstrates that this group were strongly linked with Atlantic waters, which were a richer food source than

the land. Not surprisingly, today's communities have grown up along coastal margins to benefit from the sea's bounty. The peat is cut and burnt as fuel: although arguably practical at a subsistence level, this is unjustifiable when done on a commercial scale for making briquettes and compost. Destroying bogs releases large volumes of carbon dioxide captured as the peat was laid down, and the rainfall now runs off the upland catchment areas and causes flooding in valleys and lowlands.

Connemara is unlike the adjacent region and instead is part of the Dalradian Grampian terrane extending throughout north-west Ireland. However, Connemara's position is further south than would be expected, which suggests displacement along a fault thought to have occurred in the late Ordovician (485–443 Ma). However, some suggest Connemara formed independently of the rest of the Laurentian continental margin that became the Dalradian metasediments. Green Connemara marble, a metamorphosed limestone, is found at the base of the Twelve Pins, and is a telltale trace of the forces that contorted these rocks.

10 Paps of Jura, Jura, Inner Hebrides, Argyll and Bute

The Paps of Jura are among that special order of hill to have captured the imagination of both ancient and modern people: that of the breast-shaped peak. The term 'pap' could come from the Old Norse for breast or nipple, or from the Latin *papilla*, meaning the same, and, although these hills sometimes stand alone they often come in pairs or even in threes, as seen here on Jura. From left to right they are: Beinn a' Chaolais (Mountain of the Kyle), Beinn an Òir (Mountain of Gold) – the tallest at 785m – and Beinn Shiantaidh (Holy Mountain), which is closest and appears largest. The latter two together form the classic twin peaks that gives the range their name. As with the Maiden Paps in the Scottish Borders and the Paps of Anu in Ireland, these curvaceous landforms are allied with the feminine. In the latter case the hills are directly associated with the Celtic goddess Annan or Anu. However, on Jura, as indeed in many instances, if there was a link with a specific deity then this memory has been lost.

The mountains are mostly quartzite dating from 610 Ma, which forms much of the upland scenery throughout Argyll. During the last glaciation the mountain tops remained above the ice sheet and became nunataks, or isolated rock islands surrounded by a sea of ice. These exposed rocks weather differently from those underneath the ice, which are worn smooth, and instead are attacked by frost shattering. When water seeps along a joint in the rock and then freezes, it expands putting pressure on the surrounding rock. As the joints widen and the ice thaws, more water can invade the gap and the process is repeated the next time the temperature drops. This is known as a freeze–thaw cycle and it is capable of splitting even the hardest rocks into angular blocks that now litter the mountains' sides.

11 Llanddwyn Island (Ynys Llanddwyn), Anglesey (Ynys Mon)

England, southern Ireland and Wales came into existence as a volcanic island chain, called Avalonia, in a shallow sea at the edge of a subduction zone on the northern margin of Gondwana. At first Anglesey existed separately from Wales. However, towards the end of the Precambrian it drifted towards Avalonia. As it did so the oceanic crust between them was subducted in an ocean trench and a colossal landslide tumbled the overlying rocks into the molten mix. This intriguing formation, known as the Gwna Mélange, consists of partially melted rock fragments suspended in a fine-grained matrix, and is one part of the distinctive Monian Composite terrane, which is separated from the Avalonian Composite terrane, stretching across the rest of England and Wales, by the Menai Straits Line. The mélange outcrops on Anglesey's north and west, and also reappears on land 50km across the other side of the bay on the Lleyn Peninsula, the mountains of which are seen here.

Llanddwyn protrudes finger-like into Caernarfon Bay and here the mélange includes silica-based chert, coloured pink by iron, among the dark grey pillow-basalt and limestone.

Basalt is an iron- and magnesium-rich lava and is Earth's most commonly occurring rock, as well as being the main constituent of oceanic crust. Molten basalt's disorganised crystal structure makes it behave like a liquid when it pours out of ocean trenches and from rifts on land. Its low viscosity makes it more likely to erupt, but when it does, it flows steadily rather than exploding dramatically. Llanddwyn is noted for its pillow lavas, created when cooling seawater arrests submarine basalt flows. Subsequently a skin develops, which is then inflated with more lava, forming characteristic bubbles. Basalt's crystals are nearly impossible to see with the naked eye, owing to the rapid rate at which it cools.

Like a series of unfurling fractals, kilometre-long Llanddwyn is a small island off a medium-sized one (Anglesey) next to an even larger one (Britain). Although only inaccessible at the highest of tides, Llanddwyn seems rather tenuously connected with Anglesey by a stretch of sand that has been in place only since the last ice sheet retreated. Where better for the self-imposed isolation of St Dwynwen, the daughter of the Welsh prince of Brycheiniog (Brecon)? She retreated here after turning down a marriage proposal, preferring to become a religious hermit instead. A sixteeenth-century chapel stands over the site of the one she established and a well is dedicated to her.

12 Bwa Gwyn, Rhoscolyn, Anglesey ⟹

Bwa Gwyn, the 'white arch', is named after the pale quartzite from which it is formed. Holyhead Mountain, illuminated on the far horizon, is of the same rock type, known as the Holyhead Quartzite. Throughout the Precambrian and the early Cambrian, England and Wales were largely underwater, and the quartz of the protolith was deposited at the perimeter of a shallow sea and remained free of other sediments, which has ensured the rock's purity and its light colour. When it underwent meta-morphosis, the individual quartz grains were crystalised and reorganised into an interlocking mosaic structure that is much more resistant to erosion. Despite the reconfiguration, Bwa Gwyn still exhibits the sequence of beds as they were initially laid down. However, these are now tilted into a nearly verti-cal arrangement as a result of collision between landmasses.

Arches are formed in rocky spurs that extend from cliffs when waves find and attack weaknesses between the bedded layers. Relentless erosion soon creates concave depressions at the base of the cliff line, which are then expanded to become sizeable caves before the waves eventually breach the rock and the archway is created. This is far from the end of the story, as an arch is just one stage in a process that continues when its apex collapses, leaving a pillar or lump that is completely disconnected from the cliff. As this stack is now subject to attack by waves from all directions, it is even more vulnerable to erosion and its demise is inevitable.

13 Malvern Hills, Malvern, Worcestershire

The vestiges of the Avalonian volcanic islands are found throughout central England and are encapsulated in the Malvern Hills, where the oldest rocks date to 677 Ma, making them among England's most ancient. The Malverns consist of two rock groups: metamorphosed igneous rocks formed deep within the crust, which make up most of the hills' bulk, overlain with later volcanic eruptions. Between 650 and 550 Ma, the Cadomian Orogeny raised the Avalonian terrane into mountains when collisions between volcanic island arcs, including Avalonia and the Armorican and Iberian terranes, took place on Gondwana's northern margin. By 550 Ma, Avalonia had started to drift away from Gondwana and became a separate microcontinent. As it drifted, the Rheic Ocean opened up behind it and the new landmass was eventually set on course to intercept the larger Baltica continent.

Steep-sided for their height, the Malvern name reflects their stark appearance, coming from the ancient British for 'bare hill', being similar to modern Welsh *moelfryn*. The range includes twenty-three peaks that run in an approximately 12km chain aligned north–south along the Herefordshire and Worcestershire border. The highest of these is the Worcestershire Beacon (425m), seen here illuminated. It is famous for the fires lit on the summit that can be seen for miles around. From the ridge there are expansive views east over plains leading through Gloucestershire and into Oxfordshire and, to the west, an array of rolling hills continuing through Herefordshire to the Welsh Mountains, and to the south the Bristol Channel can be glimpsed when the weather is clear.

An earthwork called the Shire Ditch cuts along most of the hills' length, threading a line along the highest part of the ridge. Although supposed to have been dug in 1287 to settle a land dispute between the Earl of Gloucester and the Bishop of Hereford, it is now known that it is a late Bronze Age track. Another notable feature is British Camp on Herefordshire Beacon (seen here in the foreground), which lies roughly midpoint along the range and which has been extensively remodelled in two phases: initially as an Iron Age hillfort, with ramparts and room for a hundred timber round houses, and then later adapted by the Romans.

14 Long Mynd & The Wrekin, Church Stretton, Shropshire

The earliest parts of the Shropshire Hills are contemporary with the Malverns, with which they share some similarities. The Wrekin, seen in the distance, is mainly composed of rhyolite (a sticky and explosively erupted lava) and tuff (from ash ejections) and is the best-known landmark in these parts. Folklore has it that the hill was created by a Welsh giant wielding a spade of earth that was to be dumped in the River Severn thereby flooding the town of Shrewsbury. *En route*, he met a cobbler who, realising the great danger, persuaded the giant that it was much too far to walk. So the soil was dumped on the plain instead, forming The Wrekin, and the mud from his oversized boots became The Ercall, immediately to the north-east. With such prominence over the surrounding plain, The Wrekin is an obvious choice for the siting of an Iron Age hillfort. The steep sides create a 2km barrier, which is reflected in the local phrase 'all round the Wrekin', meaning to go the long way around.

Closer to, the treeless ridge almost hidden by the mist is the Long Mynd (Anglicised Welsh for 'long mountain'). It is a whaleback ridge formed from shallow-water sediments, the oldest of which are the same age as the Wrekin volcanics. These rocks were shaped by repeated earthquakes resulting from the Cadomian Orogeny causing them to be lifted and folded into the steep inclines that characterise this undulating landscape known for its plunging valleys or 'batches'. The legacy of this seismic activity is the Church Stretton Fault, which runs through this area and causes occasional tremors.

The Long Mynd is one of many sites throughout Britain associated with the legendary King Arthur. The story follows the oft-repeated theme that Arthur and his knights will come to England's defence whenever war is threatened. In this variant, if one listens carefully enough to the winds passing over the moors, the sound of their galloping horses may be heard rushing in response to the danger. These heroic figures are firmly rooted in Shropshire's cultural landscape and are also linked with The Wrekin and the nearby Caer Caradoc Hill.

15 Smoo Cave, Durness, Sutherland

Smoo Cave is unique in the British Isles in that it was formed by both freshwater and seawater erosion of limestone, both of which are chemical weathering processes whereby the rock's mineral composition is altered and weakened by exposure to ions dissolved in water. A river has carved its inner recesses while the outer chamber is a tidal gorge that constitutes the largest sea cave entrance in Britain. Smoo Burn enters the cave through a wide pothole before tumbling 20m into a subterranean lake set back far beyond the reach of the waves. Archaeological investigations at the site have found both Norse and Iron Age artefacts. However, there is also some evidence to suggest that the cave was in use during the Mesolithic, not long after the most recent glaciation released its grip on the land. The word Smoo, as with many local place names, comes from the Norse and is derived from *smjuggm*, which can mean cleft or hole, although it is also interpreted as meaning hiding place.

At the dawn of the Cambrian there was an explosion in the quantity and diversity of life in the oceans heralding both a new eon, the Phanerozoic (Greek: 'visible life') and a new era, the Palaeozoic (Greek: 'ancient life'). Many marine organisms used the calcium carbonate dissolved in seawater to form hard shells and, as their remains settled on the sea floor, beds of limestone were created. Limestone can also form when calcium leached by water out of existing rocks is transported downstream before usually ending up in the sea. Once in the sea the carbonates can either combine with sediments, in which case they act as a cement binding particles together, or be deposited as calcite, an exceptionally pure form of limestone.

The Durness Limestone was laid down on a shallow marine shelf and consists of stromatolites, mound-shaped bacterial communities cemented together with calcium carbonate. The Durness rocks also include a type of limestone called dolostone, so called because of the high content of dolomite in the rock. Dolomite forms when some of the calcium is replaced with magnesium, thus making dolostone more resistant to erosion. The method by which this transformation takes place has never been observed as, although significant dolomite deposits exist in ancient sedimentary rocks, none is being laid down today. It is believed that the process took place in warm salty waters in the deep ocean. These carbonates continued to be laid down into early part of the succeeding Ordovician Period (484-443 Ma) and form a long linear margin at the eastern extent of the Hebridean terrane where it abuts the Northern Highlands.

16 The Rhinogydd, Cwm Nantcol, Gwynedd

CAMBRIAN
541–485 Ma

Early on in the Cambrian, the high ground of England and Wales was eroded by rising seas and many sediments were deposited, including the sandstones and conglomerates of the Harlech Dome, a mountainous area that once extended across Snowdonia from Snowdon in the north to Cadair Idris in the south, a distance of around 45km. The dome's core is formed from greywacke sandstone; despite being a hard-wearing rock, its great age means the mountains have all but worn away and only a few peaks remain, most notably the Rhinogydd (Anglicised to Rhinogs). On Rhinog Fawr, to the left, terraces of rock protrude like ribs through the velvet-brown mixture of heather and moorland grasses. The angle of inclination demonstrates the massive folding that raised these rocks into mountains during the Caledonian Orogeny. To the right is the Harlech Dome's apex Rhinog Fach, and separating the two peaks is a deep gully with sheer sides, the Bwlch Drws Ardudwy

or 'door to Ardudwy'. The diminutive Llyn Cwmhosan occupies a hollow above the valley floor, at the foot of the scree-covered slopes of Rhinog Fach, although to call it a lake is somewhat of an overstatement as it is little more than a large pool.

The mountains are referred to by Robert Graves in 'Letter to S.S. from Mametz Wood', a poem rich with Welsh landscape symbolism, where they are described as being like two towers marking the way to other ancient and far away places. There is something sentinel-like and darkly brooding about the Rhinogydd in the way they guard the pass, an effect that is almost certainly amplified by the remote and difficult terrain. This splendid isolation is only disturbed by the presence of one small farm at the head of the Cwm Nantcol valley over 2km away, which itself is well off the beaten track and far from the bustle of Harlech.

17 Doldrum Bay, Howth, County Dublin

Howth is at the northern end of Dublin Bay's huge crescent-shaped arc and was once an island much like the others found just offshore. It remained detached until changes in the Quaternary meant that a tombolo, a narrow beach of gravel and sand, was deposited on the island's landward-facing side. Once connected with the mainland it became a tied-island, and further deposits have coalesced on both sides of the tombolo to form tidal sandbanks.

At 171m, the Ben of Howth marks the island's highest point, and where its southern flank extends down to the sea erosion has created Doldrum Bay. Here metamorphic quartzite and sedimentary mudstone are muddled together in a mélange. However, it is possible to distinguish the separate constituents as the fine-grained mudstone is a vivid red-orange that betrays is origin in rusted sediments, whereas the quartzite – inclined on an angle – forms the luminously pale bulk of the cliffs. The latter is part of the Bray Group and it also occurs in the Wicklow

Mountains to Dublin's south, conspicuously forming the Great Sugar Loaf, a hill that can easily be seen from Howth.

It has been suggested that Doldrum comes from the Gaelic word *doltrum*, meaning grief or anguish, although this appears to be speculation. However, it may well be a reasonable association as the presence of Baily Lighthouse attests to the fact that there have been too many boats shipwrecked around this hazardous rock. The list includes the steam-powered *Queen Victoria*, which sank in a snowstorm off Howth in 1853 with the loss of eighty lives. These tragedies of the recent past are not the only stories linked with the island, as it is the setting for many a myth featuring characters ranging from sea gods and warriors to eloping lovers who sought shelter in a cave at the Ben of Howth's foot. The landscape was also featured in no less than three of James Joyce's books, perhaps most famously as the scene of Leopold Bloom's marriage proposal to Molly in *Ulysees*.

18 Schiehallion, Kinloch-Rannoch, Perthshire

Sidh Chailleann, or Schiehallion, is formed mainly from schist but it has a quartzite summit and is marked out by its regular shape, sculpted by ice flows, and its prominence over the surrounding hills. The mountain is centrally located in the Grampian Highlands and was formed around 500 Ma. It is said to be the geographical centre of Scotland, a notion supported by glancing at a map, and has an important place in the country's folklore as it was sacred to the Caledonian people who thought it to be the haunt of fairies and other nature spirits. From 1,000 BC its slopes were put to use for stalking deer and grazing sheep, a practice that continued into the nineteenth century.

In 1774 the mountain was the location of a groundbreaking physical experiment to work out the Earth's weight that was carried out by Astronomer Royal Nevil Maskelyne assisted by mathematician Charles Hutton. The procedure was to first establish what fraction of the Earth was represented by the mountain using the Earth's circumference in combination with a measurement of Newton's gravitational constant, calculated using pendulums. From this they could determine the mountain's mass, which was then used to estimate the mass of the entire planet. The experiment was replicated in 2005 and completed in a day, whereas it took Maskelyne and Hutton seventeen weeks. In the course of the original experiment Hutton devised what later became known as contour lines to represent the surveyed heights of the mountain, making it the first landform to be mapped in such a way.

CAMBRIAN/
ORDOVICIAN

19 Rhobell Fawr, near Dolgellau, Gwynedd

The crust beneath the Iapetus Ocean was undergoing subduction throughout the late Cambrian and Ordovician periods, which brought the American and European plates closer together. The melting of the crust was the trigger for volcanic activity on both Avalonia and Laurentia's continental margins. This gave rise to the highest mountains in Snowdonia, the Lake District and County Mayo. Rhobell Fawr was created around 510 Ma as an island volcano rising steeply from deep waters, and producing basaltic lava and large volumes of ash. Today the extinct volcano is the only substantial remnant of this period of arc igneous activity in Wales.

Although, at 734m, Rhobell Fawr is not especially high by Snowdonia's standards. It exists well separated from the surrounding mountains and offers expansive views across the region. To the west it is bounded by the vestiges of the Harlech Dome in the form of the Cambrian Rhinogydds, to the north-west is Snowdon and Cadair Idris lies to the south. Unlike these other mountains, Rhobell Fawr lacks a dramatic summit and its attractions are much more subtle. There are some areas where the grass is interrupted by rocky outcrops, including these weathered patches of dolerite, seen emerging from the hilltop like petrified scales. Dolerite is an igneous rock similar to basalt; however, unlike extrusive basalt, intrusive dolerite forms sills which are horizontal seams formed parallel to the bedding, and dykes which are long narrow structures that can be steeply inclined or nearly vertical. Nature abhors a vacuum and where gaps open in rocks, either between sedimentary beds or as a result of faulting, pressurised magma will find a way to squeeze through any space it can.

20 Grey Crags and Skiddaw, Borrowdale Valley, Cumbria

Skiddaw, although the fourth highest of England's mountains, has little in the way of exciting summit geology being smooth and grass-covered on top. However there are some exposed rocks along the ridges and slopes leading to it, including the brittle-looking slate of Grey Crags overhanging the steep scree on Skiddaw's western flank. The name is thought to come from the Cumbric *sgwyddau*, which is similar to the modern Welsh word for shoulder, *ysgwydd*. When the main summit and Little Man – an outlying peak to the south-east – are viewed together from certain angles it needs little imagination to see them as shoulders. The Brythonic language, from which both Cumbric and Welsh derive, was once spoken right across northern England, as far as the Scottish Borders, which accounts for the Welsh-sounding names in the Lake District.

The Skiddaw Group slates are the oldest rocks found in the Lake District. These metamorphosed mudstones originally derived from erosion of Avalonia's continental mass and the resulting sediments being deposited on the continent's coastal margin. This characteristic grey slate is encountered throughout the villages of Borrowdale (and beyond), where it is a common building material, a choice that is not only practical but links the structures sympathetically with the landscape. In fact it is one of the two main rock groups to be found in the Lake District, the other being the Borrowdale Volcanics.

Skiddaw's slate has also been used somewhat more unconventionally in the construction of a lithophone, a musical instrument similar to a xylophone. Local inventor Peter Crosthwaite discovered, while out walking one summer's day in 1785, that slates from the mountain have a harmonious quality that can be shaped and tuned to perfection. It took him thirteen years to source and process the rock needed to create what became known as the 'Musical Stones of Skiddaw', and it was much celebrated in its day. This lithophone is now housed in the Keswick Museum and Art Gallery.

ORDOVICIAN
485–443 Ma

ORDOVICIAN
485–443 Ma

21 Devil's Chair, Stiperstones, Shropshire

The Stiperstones is a distinctive ridge aligned south-west to north-east, overlooking the village of the same name to the west and the nearby Long Mynd and the other Shropshire Hills to the east. Along its length there are six outcrops of Stiperstones Quartzite, which is harder and therefore more prominent than the rocks underlying the surrounding moor. The Devil's Chair is the most northerly in this sequence of tors rising from piles of loose stone – split by frost-shattering – scattered, often knee-deep among the heather, which gives some idea of the ridge's former extent.

The oddly shaped outcrops are a notable horizon feature and many tales have become attached to them. None more so than to the Devil's Chair, the largest of the group, where the Dark One himself is reputed to hold court over his followers, both the earthbound and the ethereal, who gather once a year to choose their king. It goes without saying that it was the Devil who brought the stones here. In a variation on a familiar story, Satan was on his way to fill a valley known as Hell's Gutter with stones held in his apron when they spilled out, and rather than picking them up he decided to leave them where they fell. The Devil's Chair is also the reputed haunt of Wild Edric, a Saxon earl who defied the conquering Normans for a time before finally losing his lands. In a narrative recalling King Arthur's association with the Long Mynd and other local hills, Edric will supposedly ride out whenever England is threatened by invasion.

Penmaen Dewi, or St David's Head, overlooks Cardigan Bay and is mainly formed from a band of igneous gabbro, a rock that, although chemically equivalent to basalt is intrusive rather than eruptive. Classed as a mafic rock, a silicate high in iron and magnesium, it is the oxidised iron that stains the boulders rust-coloured. Gabbro has crystals big enough to see with the naked eye as surrounding rocks insulate the magma, allowing it to cool more gradually and permitting larger crystals to develop. At St David's Head the gabbro was intruded into early Ordovician sedimentary beds, in this case slate, during the middle of that same period. As slate is only a lightly metamorphosed rock it is less able to resist erosion than hard gabbro, which means that much of it has been eaten away by the sea thus creating numerous inlets; so it is no surprise that the headland's highest point Carn Llidi (181m) is also part of the gabbro intrusion.

This isolated location, which is about as far west in Wales as it is possible to go, was an important place in Prehistoric times. Many Neolithic structures have been unearthed, including a field system leading from the west-facing and presumably sunny slopes of Carn Llidi down towards the sea. Settlements existed alongside the fields and these communities established chambered burial cairns on top of Carn Llidi. They also built the Coetan Arthur burial cairn at the end of the peninsula. Just a few metres to the south there is the ruined Iron-Age fort known as Clawdd y Milwyr, or Warrior's Dyke, perched on the cliff edge just 35m above the waves, but spacious enough to have seven or eight stone round-houses within its walls. Despite this early settlement, which is thought to have continued into the Romano-British period, the landscape has since been left uncultivated, changing little in the last 2,000 years.

23 Carn Menyn, Preseli Hills, Pembrokeshire

Carn Menyn is part of the Mynydd Preseli (Preseli Mountains), a chain of meandering rounded hills connected by a ridge. They extend from Cerrig Lladron in the west, continuing via Foel Feddau – both of which are marked with prehistoric cairns – past Bedd Arthur Neolithic circle, and through an area of many separate rock outcrops, including Carn Menyn, before reaching Foel Drygarn where there is yet another cairn and also a hillfort. The early inhabitants of this area seem to have recognised the physical relationship between these hills and endowed it with some level of meaning. On a 1:25,000 map the alignment of bare hilltop, rock landforms and man-made additions becomes even more obvious, especially as a dotted footpath line threads between each feature.

Carn Menyn was the site of a Neolithic quarry where the distinctive local rock, spotted dolerite, was extracted. Axes made from it have been found throughout the British Isles. Freshly cut spotted dolerite is an attractive colour giving rise to the alternative 'Preseli Bluestone' name. The rock is exceptionally hard, making quarrying of it difficult, so the name Carn Menyn,

translating as 'Butter Rock', seems amusingly inappropriate. However, such an association is not unusual and there are many topographical features connected with dairy and other aspects of farming throughout the British Isles.

What makes these rocks particularly special is that they were used extensively in the construction of Stonehenge. It is still a matter of some debate as to how the stones got all the way from west Wales to Wiltshire. Some maintain that the monument's builders dragged the many tonnes of rock required all that way. However, there is strong evidence to suggest that nature helped by dumping them close to their current location on the Salisbury Plain in the wake of a retreating glacier. Perhaps it was simply lucky that these large boulders happened to be available locally. Is it serendipitous that the dolerite cleaves to frost-shattering into ready-formed menhirs (the upright component of stone circles) or was Stonehenge specifically designed with these tall stones in mind? Bluestones have been found to have interesting acoustic properties and that may well have been a contributing factor to their use in a ceremonial setting.

24 Pen Anglas, near Fishguard, Pembrokeshire

At the end of the precarious point, in rocks dipping steeply towards the sea, there is a fine slab of dolerite exhibiting the peculiar spectacle of columnar jointing in cross-section. Manifesting as hexagons, pentagons and other polygonal shapes, this is one of the strangest guises that igneous rock can assume and is most famously seen in the basalts of the Giant's Causeway and Fingal's Cave (see pages 160–3). The phenomenon is due to the rate at which the lava cools, and if it happens evenly enough, regular columns are formed. Shrinkage causes them to crack along the joints, revealing a tessellated configuration resembling honeycomb. This is essentially similar to the pattern seen when wet mud dries out and contracts.

There is a fundamental principle at work here providing an insight into nature's energy efficiency. The reason these columns are mainly hexagonal is because it is the most economic shape to produce in this context. A sphere is the simplest of all shapes as it is one sided and has the smallest surface area. When many spheres such as soap bubbles, for example, of similar size merge, the spaces between them collapse to form straight-sided walls and, if the bubbles did not inevitably pop, they would organise themselves into an interlocking hexagonal structure. While this is true at the atomic scale and in ultra-organised honey-bee hives, it is not always achieved with large-scale patterns subject to external events, hence the varied geometry seen in these rocks.

25 Mweelrea and Killary Harbour, border of County Mayo and Galway

At 814m, Mweelrea is the highest point in Connacht, one of the four historical Irish provinces, which includes the counties of Galway, Leitrim, Mayo, Roscommon and Sligo. The mountain was formed in a small ocean basin, called the South Mayo Trough, situated close to a volcanic island arc. These volcanoes erupted no fewer than five times and produced rhyolitic tuffs interspersing varied sedimentary beds laid down in deep water. These beds consist of sandstone, slate and conglomerate made up mainly of cobbles. The basin is known to have existed for around 25 million years, during which time thick layers of sand and mud were deposited. The upper beds are coarse sandstone formed in rivers feeding into a delta that emptied into the basin, although by this point it was nearly choked by accumulating sediments.

Rising directly from the sea Mweelrea or 'smooth bald hill' is a sheer-walled slab of a mountain with little vegetation growing on it. The walls are made so vertiginous by the long and narrow Killary Harbour fjord that cuts

along the mountain's base. As one of three fjords in Ireland, and at 16km long and up to 45m deep, it was carved by glaciers flowing from higher ground on their way to the sea. Because they are created by the long-term presence of ice, such geomorphological features are associated with far northern and southern latitudes. Most led to the ocean and became flooded when sea levels rose, although they can also form freshwater lakes where glacial moraine (eroded debris) has blocked access to the sea.

Killary Harbour runs along the Doon Rock Fault in the Silurian sedimentary rocks forming this foreshore, separating the contrasting rocks of the Mweelrea Mountains to the north (which are part of the early to mid Ordovician rocks of the South Mayo Trough) from Connemara's Dalradian terrane that includes the Twelve Pins just a short distance to the south. The fjord also creates a natural divide along which the county line between Galway and Mayo is drawn.

26 The Saddle, Cadair Idris, Gwynedd

The eruptions that started with Rhobell Fawr, only 12km to the north-east, continued in dramatic style with the creation of Cadair Idris. The mountain is chiefly composed of tuffs formed during an unimaginably explosive volcanic event that would have ricocheted around the world. A *nuée ardente*, from the French for 'glowing cloud' on account of the lightning generated inside the pyroclastic flow, is the most devastating type of eruption where ash, rock fragments and gas together behave like an exceptionally dense liquid, which moves so fast that there is little chance of getting out of the way. Thrown high into the atmosphere and creating a mushroom-shaped cloud all too reminiscent of an atomic explosion, the particles eventually settle to form ignimbrites, which, when lithified, are known as tuffs.

Cyfrwy, or The Saddle, is the dramatic crest on Cadair Idris' western tip and is an arête, which is a type of ridge created when two glaciers on either side bite deeply into the mountain to form a knife-edge. The ridge continues as a curving wall, like the high back of a chair, enclosing a theatrical space that makes a perfect stage for legendary exploits. One theory maintains that Cadair Idris, or 'The Chair of Idris', takes its name from one of the Kings of Meirionydd, Idris ap Gwyddno, who fought a battle on the mountain. Another claims it was named after an astronomer-giant who was reputed to use the bowl shaped valley and mountainside as his seat, from which he looked out at the stars. It is still said that anyone spending the night alone on Cadair Idris will either go mad, be inspired to become a philosopher or possibly a poet.

27 Glyder Fach from Bwlch Tryfan, Conwy

The Glyderau, often known as The Glyders, are the third highest range in Snowdonia and are composed of the same tuffs as those forming The Saddle, so the physical similarities between these mountains is obvious. Bwlch Tryfan, the boulder-choked gully between Glyder Fach and Tryfan, the adjacent peak, is around 800m high so it is perhaps the last place one would expect to find a dry stone wall. Yet here is an enclosure built on top of a natural outcrop that is seen to extend part-way up Glyder Fach's steep northern face, illustrating just how far into the mountains sheep-farming extended. The practice of clearing stones to improve pasture dates back to the dawn of agriculture. However, these loose stones were later put to use in building enclosure walls, some of which are of thirteenth-century origin, but most date back to the eighteenth century.

Throughout the eighteenth and early part of the nineteenth centuries, these mountains were used for grazing in the summer months when farmers would have a seasonal base called a 'hafod' and, in the winter, they would return with their flock to the lowlands or coastal areas where the farms were known as 'hendre'. Today the combination of poor soils and harsh weather conditions make this part of Snowdonia fit only for raising sheep. However, there is archaeological evidence of cultivation strips associated with arable farming, some of which are found surprisingly high up, which suggests climate and soil fertility have deteriorated over time.

28 Snowdon and Glaslyn, Gwynedd ⇒

Wales' highest mountain provides an unexpected clue to its marine origins right at the summit. At the start of the Ordovician, most life was confined to warm, shallow seas, and brachiopods, scuttling trilobites and large cephalopods - the ancient ancestors of the nautilus - dominated the marine environment. Although some animals and plants began to explore coastal margins, they ventured no further than sandy shorelines. Brachiopods, a type of mollusc that spent their lives anchored to the sea floor, once thrived here. Their existence was cut short when volcanoes, including Rhobell Fawr and Cadair Idris to the south as well as these in northern Snowdonia, belched out hot ash that buried them under a layer of suffocating sludge. Once entombed, they were subsequently raised up to mountain height as a result of the Caledonian Orogeny, the Grampian phase of which began not long after these rocks were laid down.

Snowdon has the dubious honour of being one of the wettest places in the British Isles, as atmospheric currents usually blow in from the west bringing moist air from the neighbouring Atlantic Ocean. The plentiful rain keeps the many lakes dotted around the range replenished. Glaslyn, or 'blue lake', is directly below the summit and is allegedly haunted by the Afanc, a hybrid freshwater monster straight out of Welsh mythology. The Afanc is alleged to flood not only valleys but to drown unsuspecting passers by as well. One of its kind was reputedly slain by that other elusive figure, King Arthur. The Afanc's origin goes further back than that of the Loch Ness Monster but is much less well known. Perhaps Nessie endures more readily in our collective consciousness as the suspension of disbelief is proportionate to the volume of water. Loch Ness is vast whereas Glaslyn is just too small to hide a prehistoric relic of beastly dimensions.

29 Helvellyn, Glenridding, Cumbria

Helvellyn rises to 950m above sea level and the range forms the highest ground in the Lake District's Eastern Fells. These mountains are part of the Borrowdale Volcanic Group, a suite of rocks centring upon the Borrowdale Valley in the Central Fells, and also appearing in the Southern Fells. These are thick lavas issued from island volcanoes and account for most of the region's highest peaks. Helvellyn itself includes andesitic lavas, tuffs and volcaniclastic sandstone – a sedimentary rock created from a mixture of ash and other ejected fragments.

The range, with Helvellyn at its apex, forms a 10km ridge running from Dollywagon Pike in the south, north-westwards to Clough Head. Seen from a westerly aspect it appears massive rather than dramatic and as Alfred Wainwright put it in Book One of his seminal guides to the Lakeland Fells, 'It is a great pity that Helvellyn is usually ascended by its western routes, for this side is unattractive and lacking in interest'. The eastern approach is much more striking, as from this direction the mountain appears to reach down with enclosing arms

either side of Red Tarn, presenting the walker with a choice of two perilously sheer arêtes leading to the summit: Striding Edge to the left and Swirall Edge to the right. Striding Edge is notorious as the scene of many a false footstep, usually in winter conditions, although its fearsome reputation is built on the law of averages. Considering that Helvellyn is so accessible and a large number of people attempt the climb, it is not surprising that some fall victim to the mountain's fickle charms.

As with Glaslyn below, Snowdon Red Tarn is a drowned corrie, which is an approximately circular valley carved when a glacier flanking a mountain slowly rotates and abrades the rock. The same process produces arêtes along upper edges and the two forms are usually seen together. The eastern side of the Helvellyn range manifests no fewer than six corries, displayed as coves on the map, over a distance of only 4km. Corrie is from the Gaelic for cooking pot and refers to the bowl-like form. In Wales they are known as cwms, although confusingly not everything marked as such is necessarily a corrie, as cwm is the generic word for valley.

30 Great Gable, Wasdale, Cumbria

Great Gable lies at the head of the Wasdale valley and is a continuation of the Borrowdale Volcanic Group that here forms the roof of the Southern Fells. At 899m, Great Gable is not the highest of Wasdale's peaks, losing out to its near neighbours Scafell (964m) and Scafell Pike (978m) – England's tallest mountains. However, it has the greatest visual presence when seen from the valley's entrance. The mountain not only has an almost symmetrical profile but occupies a prominent and central position framed by Kirk Fell on one side and Lingmell on the other. Together they create a scene of such classic proportions that of all the possible picturesque choices in the region it is this view that is represented in the Lake District National Park logo.

Closer to, Great Gable becomes altogether more daunting and its challenging character is attributable to the heavily eroded andesitic lavas, tuffs and agglomerated rocks from which it is formed. From high up on the path over Gavel Neese, the pointed profile of the White Napes and the jagged outline of the Great Napes crowd the skyline. In the gap between them, known as Little Hell Gate, is a small scree that is part of the feared Climber's Traverse, which leaves the main footpath at this point to skirt below these ominous looking crags *en route* to the Napes Needle. The latter is a protruding pinnacle that has become synonymous with W.P. Haskett-Smith, one of the early popularisers of rock-climbing, who ascended the 20m formation in 1886 without ropes.

ORDOVICIAN
485–443 Ma

31 Wastwater, Wasdale, Cumbria

Wastwater is a long, narrow ribbon-lake nearly filling Wasdale and is almost surrounded, with mountains on three sides. Among these is Illgill Head, rising immediately above the lake, also known as The Screes because of the chunks of rock covering a large percentage of the mountain and continuing below the waterline. The presence of the scree slope is a clue to the lake's origin as both are features associated with glaciation. The loose stone tumbling off Wasdale's mountains provides plenty of material for the patchwork of field enclosures stretching along a valley floor smoothed flat by an evenly distributed layer of glacial till - the unsorted sediments and angular fragments dumped as melting ice retreats. Although the valley greatly benefits from the shelter provided by the high peaks, the wet weather in this part of the world means that the land is only really suitable for raising livestock.

The lake's name is from Old Norse *vatnsdalr*, meaning valley of the water, and is England deepest lake descending to 79m, about 15m of which is below sea level. The reason for this is that when a glacier carved its way through these high mountains some time between 50,000 and 10,000 years ago, it over-deepened the valley, creating a rock basin that subsequently flooded. These depressions occur when abrasive rocks trapped at the bottom of the moving glacier scour bedrock of alternating layers, eroding any softer material first and leaving the harder rocks relatively intact, which then act like a dam. Because of the lake's tremendous depth the waters are exceptionally cold, and clear due to the lack of nutrients, so in spite of its size it supports a limited amount of life.

A glacial episode took place at the end of the Ordovician as a consequence of falling atmospheric carbon dioxide levels. As the ice at the South Pole expanded, it locked away water from the world's oceans, causing the level to drop significantly, thus destroying the ecological niches that had been so successfully exploited by marine organisms. More than 60 per cent of marine invertebrates died out and, as nearly all life was confined to the oceans, this was a devastating event, second only to the Permian-Triassic extinction (discussed later).

32 Howgill Fells, Cumbria

In the shrinking Iapetus Ocean between Avalonia and Laurentia, the settling marine sediments derived from the eroding continents became mudstone, sandstone and shale. By the start of the Silurian, Avalonia had joined with Baltica (creating Avalonia-Baltica) and as this new landmass drifted towards Laurentia the ocean basin that lay between them buckled and was lifted to mountain height. This raised ocean floor is today seen in the uplands lying between the Lake District and the Yorkshire Dales, which include the extensive Howgill Fells at the highest point. These hills have rounded summits and are typically featureless save for a thick blanket of peat, although one notable exception is Cautley Crag hewn into the side of The Calf that, at 676m, is the tallest of the Howgill Fells. In this impressive kilometre-long escarpment situated high above the valley floor the blocky core of these lumpy hills is revealed.

Red Gill Beck runs off The Calf and cuts through the northern end of the crag before tumbling over the edge to form Cautley Spout waterfall. Although it is not one unbroken drop, Cautley Spout descends for a respectable 198m in total, making it England's highest waterfall above ground. An obvious, if at times alarmingly steep, route up to the fells runs alongside the beck closely following the tiers of rock breaking the water's cascade. An Iron Age settlement existed a stone's throw away from Cautley Spout's base and while this community was not unusual, displaying the typical layout of fields and roundhouses, the site does include an curious element: a stone-edged track leading in a straight line from the settlement to the waterfall. The effort and resources necessary for such a construction would suggest that Cautley Spout had more than just a practical use, and may have had ritual significance, perhaps enhanced by the awe-inspiring setting. Rivers are universally accredited by ancient cultures as sources of life and good health.

33 The Grey Man of Merrick, Dumfries and Galloway

It could be argued that if you stare at any rocks for too long that oddly anthropomorphic qualities will begin to emerge. However, the Grey Man's human visage is so strikingly obvious that he must have affected people's psyche throughout the ages. The Grey Man is a mimetolith: a rock formation that resembles something identifiable, also known as a simulacrum. Sited on crags below Merrick in an out-of-the-way location well past the point at which the footpath ends, he is not easy to find so the discovery induces a feeling of having stumbled off the map only to arrive in another dimension that is more fantastical than the one left behind.

Merrick is the highest peak in the Range of the Awful Hand (also named for its mimeolithic qualities) and is within the Southern Uplands area of hills running from the North Channel off Scotland's south-western coast to St Abb's Head and the North Sea to the north-east. The Southern Upland Fault delineates the area's northern limit, while to the south lies the Iapetus Suture which is the belt marking where Avalonia-Baltica merged with Laurentia, connecting the northern and southern fragments of the British Isles. The Grey Man's angular features are etched into rocks formed from sediments scraped off the floor of the Iapetus Ocean and heaped up onto the shores of Laurentia as the two continents closed in on one another. The rocks were then metamorphosed by close proximity to the granite that subsequently formed in this area during the Devonian period.

SIULURIAN
443–419 Ma

34 Constitution Hill (Craig-glais), Aberystwyth, Ceredigion

Much of central Wales is formed from mudstones and sandstones that were deposited in the Welsh Basin when Avalonia lay beneath a shallow sea. At Constitution Hill there is a particularly well exposed section of rapidly alternating beds of greywacke, deposited during a submarine avalanche, and mudstone repeated throughout the 100m high cliffs. The sequence is named the Aberystwyth Grits, in recognition of the location's importance, and it was one of the first places where this type of deposition was studied.

The strata were created by a series of underwater landslides carrying sediments into the deep ocean. They can happen where a river delta transports sediment to the sea or a lake, and either an earthquake or the accumulation of weight triggers a collapse, creating a dense flow known as a turbidity current. The steeper the slope the faster the flow, and speeds can reach up to 600 km

per hour or half the speed of sound. The first sediments laid down are usually unsorted and contain large particles. However, as the current slows and becomes less dense the deposits become finer. Typically, once the turbidity current has ceased the deposited layers are overlain with fine silt and mud. If this is covered by sediments from another landside and the cycle repeated, then a stack of alternating beds is built up.

During the early Devonian Period (419–359 Ma), these beds, along with earlier deposits within the Welsh Basin, were folded and forced upwards. Because the greywacke is harder than the mudstone, the cliffs took on a stepped appearance as they eroded at different rates. The tilting of the cliffs is just the right angle to invite ascent by the foolhardy, as though it were some improbable staircase. Not that this can or should be recommended.

35 Croagh Patrick/Cruach Phádraig, County Mayo

Croagh Patrick is one of the key landforms within Ireland's north-western terrane and is mainly composed of a sequence of quartzite rocks underlain by Precambrian material. Geologically, it is related to the Twelve Pins of Connemara. It has an almost conical summit, especially when seen from the east, upon a bulky ridge that rises steeply above the younger rocks of low-lying Clew Bay (see pages 178–9).

For centuries, the mountain has been dedicated to St Patrick, Ireland's patron saint, and this is little surprise considering its commanding presence. However, as with so many religious matters, the story is a little more complicated than it first appears, as Croagh Patrick was sacred long before Christianity arrived in Ireland early in the fifth century. Medieval monks recorded that the mountain was previously known as Cruachan Aigli, or Eagle Rock, and a Neolithic petroglyph-marked boulder bearing cup-and-ring carvings is found on the peak's eastern slopes. Croagh Patrick was also the focus for a fertility rite that took place during the Lughnasa festival, when any woman struggling to conceive could climb the mountain on the first day of August and spend a night under the stars. The late summer Lughnasa festival celebrated the harvest and was associated with fecundity – as some of the wilder tales relate.

An annual pilgrimage up Croagh Patrick in honour of the saint is attended by tens of thousands of people and takes place on the last Sunday in July, known as Garland or Reek Sunday. The date may have shifted slightly as a result of changing from the Julian to Gregorian calendars, and the meaning has changed, but the original subtext is intact. It was not until AD 414 that St Patrick is reputed to have spent forty days and forty nights on the summit throughout Lent, during which time he famously banished from Ireland all the snakes and the demons with which they were associated, and symbolically ousted the old gods from their mountain-top seats of power. Identifying earlier deities with Christian saints and the building of churches on existing sacred sites, as on Croagh Patrick, is widespread throughout Britain and Ireland. The original pilgrimage took place in the dark, although this has fallen out of favour in today's more safety-conscious times and, although it is discouraged, the exceptionally devoted still walk barefoot over the punishing quartzite scree as an act of penance.

SIULURIAN
443–419 Ma

36 Wenlock Edge, Church Stretton, Shropshire

Wenlock Edge is an example of 'vale and scarp' scenery, and although it extends for a substantial 24km, its attractions are subtle. This type of landscape is defined by its long parallel ridges separated by narrow valleys and can be seen repeated across much of lowland Britain. At 330m above sea level, Wenlock Edge is dwarfed by the Clee Hills to the south-east, of which Brown Clee Hill (540m) is seen here. From a glance it is impossible to guess that the largely wooded ridge was originally a late Silurian coral reef that developed in a shallow sea with warm clear waters. A rise in sea level during this period, due to melt waters from Ordovician glaciers, meant that much land was under shallow seas. These conditions were so favourable that reefs were capable of growing to a great size, creating the basis for a whole new ecosystem that, for the first time, included bony fish. Meanwhile, on land, plants took hold on riverbanks, estuaries and lake margins, forming Earth's first wetland environments. The corals of Wenlock Edge are different from those seen in today's reefs as these earlier species have long since become extinct.

The Wenlock name, in part, probably refers to the creamy whiteness of the limestone that is most apparent when freshly exposed. 'Wen' is thought to come from the Welsh for white, *gwyn*. However, the meaning of 'lock' is less certain as it could stem from *loc*, Old Welsh for monastery, or possibly from *loca*, meaning an enclosed space, both of which have the Latin word for place, *locus*, at their root. This location is not only geologically important, having given its name to the Wenlock epoch, it is also a cultural icon that has inspired the likes of poet A.E. Housman, composer Ralph Vaughan Williams and the artist L.S. Lowry. Some landscapes, be they understated or extraordinary, exert a charismatic hold over certain people and plant the seeds of greatness within their minds.

37 Clogher Head, Dingle Peninsula/Corca Dhuibhne, County Kerry

In the late Silurian, around 425 Ma, the closing act in the merging of Avalonia-Baltica with Laurentia occurred, and by the end of the period the once vast Iapetus Ocean had been squeezed out of all existence. During the collision, which continued for another 25 million years, the Caledonian Mountains were raised all along the margin. The Dingle Peninsula, the furthest point west on the Irish mainland and the edge of Western Europe, is only a little way south of the suture line on the Avalonian side. The line runs roughly halfway between the peninsula and the Shannon Estuary, which is about 50km to the north, and can be followed to Clogherhead (a different one) on the east coast, reaching Scotland at the Solway Firth and exiting near Holy Island close to the English/Scottish border. Although the suture is not always easy to trace, its exact location can be determined by analysing the abrupt transition between the different fossils originating on each continent.

From Clogher Head the view north includes bays and headlands formed from Lower Silurian sandstones and siltstones that come in colours ranging from grey through purple to orange. These beds form craggy Sybil Point

(left) and the diminutive yet distinctive Three Sisters hills (middle), which from the left are called Binn Hanrai, An Bhinn Mheánach and Binn Diarmada. Interestingly, despite their collective attribution, none has a female name associated with it. Clogher Head itself mainly consists of the same deposits originally laid down on a shallow sea floor that was gradually uplifted as a complete unit, and left relatively undeformed by the subduction of the Iapetus' oceanic crust descending southwards directly beneath them. However, evidence of the landmasses closing in on one another is seen in the Clogher Head Anticline, which is an upwards fold (like an arch) where the oldest beds are at the core.

The jagged pale grey rocks appearing uppermost on Clogher Head are rhyolitic tuffs from periodic eruptions of a small volcanic island arc triggered by the subducting crust. These ejections covered the region in fine ash, ignimbrites and occasional lava flows. Stone tools fashioned from the rhyolite dating back to 4,000 BC have been found at Ferriters Cove, the inlet directly in front of Sybil Point.

38 Siccar Point, Berwickshire

To the untrained eye this may simply appear to be some red rocks next to some grey ones, yet these unassuming masses of different sandstones offer an insight into the slow pace of planetary processes. In 1788 Siccar Point was to become one of the world's most important geological sites when geologists James Hutton and Sir James Hall, along with fellow scientist John Playfair, set out in a boat to examine the Berwickshire coastline. What they discovered at Siccar Point would eventually become known as one of Hutton's Unconformities. Three years earlier in 1785 Hutton had given two talks at the Royal Society of Edinburgh on his *Theory of the Earth* text, in which he drew upon twenty-five years' study to argue the case for Uniformitarianism. The theory proposed by Charles Lyell, the foremost geologist of his day, states that the incremental processes observable today are the same ones that have shaped the Earth in the past and that they unfold over a huge length of time. This has been critical to our understanding of Earth's evolution, although it does not take into account catastrophic events such as a sudden increase in volcanic activity or large-scale meteor impacts.

Siccar Point consists of marine greywacke sandstone, dating from the Silurian, overlain by Old Red Sandstone (ORS) from the succeeding Devonian period. Hutton observed that the greywacke had had time to be laid down on the sea bed, lifted to a vertical orientation by earth movements and exposed to the air, eroded by rain, wind and the sea, all before the ORS was deposited, which itself then underwent uplift and erosion. He considered this ultimate proof of the theory and he went on to publish his paper in 1788. At the time many believed the Earth was just 6,000 years old, based on the genealogies of the Bible. Hutton was suggesting this gap in the layers alone represented more than that, and for this reason his conclusions were considered controversial. To this day there are those who dispute the validity of Uniformitarianism.

SILURIAN/
DEVONIAN

39 Kintra, Isle of Mull, Inner Hebrides

Intense crustal melting at the base of the newly uplifted Caledonian Mountains saw the creation of granites on both sides of the Iapetus Suture. These silica-rich rocks formed deep inside the mountain belt within magma chambers known as plutons. On Mull the granite was intruded into the Moinian rocks of the Northern Highlands, and the island is the most southerly outpost of this terrane. Granite is exceptionally tough and it can be identified by its medium-to-large crystals produced by slow cooling of the magma, which gives the rock an abrasive character. Plutons are revealed only through the subsequent erosion of covering rocks, and they frequently denote the position of long-vanished fold mountains. Plutons are appropriately named after Pluto, ruler of the underworld in ancient Greek mythology, and the word volcanic stems from Vulcan, the Roman god of fire, who was associated with all things flammable, including volcanoes and lightning.

Kintra's rocks are part of the Ross of Mull granite that spreads across an area of more than 30km^2, although half of this is under the sea. Weathering has created the combination of deep joints and rounded edges, which is an identifying feature of granite. The scale of these forms (the area shown is approximately 2 x 6m) is indicated by the sea thrift managing to grow in crevices where soil is scant and also acidic (from the breakdown of granite), while tolerating the brine-soaked environment. The Ross of Mull granite is pink from the high percentage of potassium feldspar it contains, and also has flecks of black mica and smoky quartz crystals. These attractive qualities have made it a popular construction stone, and the Tòrr Mor quarry at Fionnphort has provided material for buildings as far away as New Zealand.

40 The Three Sisters, Bidean nam Bian, Glen Coe, Lochaber, Highlands

The Scottish Highlands were located within the Caledonian Mountain belt that continued to rise throughout the Silurian. Granites forming within the mountains were later followed by huge outpourings of lava and ash above ground. These extrusive rocks were once present across the Scottish Highlands but have now been almost completely eroded away. One of the two areas where they can still be seen is in the impressive surroundings of Glen Coe. This was the location of what has popularly become known as a supervolcano – like the one waiting to go off under Yellowstone National Park – and there were five eruptions here on a cataclysmic scale, each of which ejected 1,000m³ of magma.

The Three Sisters of Glen Coe are carved from thick outpourings of rhyolite that smothered the previous eruptions of andesite, which is a mixture of runny basaltic and viscous rhyolitic magma. Each 'sister' is a spur extending from Bidean nam Bian (the area's highest summit at 1,150m), which has been truncated by a passing glacier. This exposure has provided a view of where the two rocks meet, and the demarcation between them is obvious as the darker andesite is more heavily vegetated than the lighter-coloured rhyolite, which forms the nearby boulder and is above the snow line on the mountains.

That these rocks have survived at all is due to a dramatic event known as cauldron subsidence. When a volcano's magma chamber completely empties the overlying rocks, now unsupported, fall into the void and create a caldera, which is a circular-basin crater measuring 10km or more across. This meant that the layers of andesite and rhyolite were subsumed into the surrounding rocks, which gave them some protection from the passing ice and now these entombing rocks have worn away. Glencoe was recognised as a caldera in 1909 and was the second one in the world to be identified – the first being the island of Santorini in the Mediterranean.

41 Buachaille Etive Mor, Glen Etive/Glen Coe, Lochaber, Highland

Buachaille Etive Mor, or the Great Herdsman of Etive, stands tall at the northern entrance to Glen Etive, with no flock to tend other than the roving herds of Red Deer inhabiting the lonely moor. At 1,022m, it is nearly 130m shorter than Bidean nam Bian but despite that is no less impressive. Although these mountains share the same origin, their forms appear different, particularly when seen from the east. Buachaille Etive Mor is the archetypal mountain: the central buttress is an almost perfectly triangular slab and is vertiginously steep. Its fame is assured by the fact that it is a lowlander's first impression of Glen Coe when arriving from the south via the A82 and, even on the dreariest of days, the road's many lay-bys are dotted with camera-wielding tourists keen to capture something of its magnificent presence.

The valley floor is a saturated blanket bog drained by many rivers where boulders of various sizes have been polished smooth by torrents of water. Eroded component crystals are seen scattered along the riverbed where they form sandy sediments. Plutonic and volcanic rocks are found alongside each other and are easily confused as both the granite and, unusually, the rhyolite have a pinkish hue. However, the spherical stone seen here can be identified as granite by its prominent crystals, whereas rhyolite's crystals are not obvious to the naked eye and andesite is considerably darker. Granite and rhyolite are chemically similar and they belong to the felsic group, which is high in silica and aluminium. However, andesite is an intermediate rock as it is combined with mafic (iron-magnesium) magma.

42 Ben Nevis and Càrn Mòr Dearg, Glen Nevis, Lochaber, Highland

Ben Nevis is located directly to the south of the Great Glen Fault, the course of which is indicated by a series of lochs, including Loch Ness. The fault divides the Dalradian Grampian Highlands, in which Ben Nevis is situated, from the Moinian Northern Highlands, effectively separating north-west Scotland from the south-east. It is a conservative plate boundary equivalent to the San Andreas Fault in California and was last properly active around 350 Ma. Formed during the Caledonian Orogeny's final stages, it is further evidence of the collision that ultimately created Ben Nevis, the main bulk of which is granite intruded into metamorphic schists as a series of concentrically arranged ring dykes. In common with Glen Coe, a short distance to the south, major volcanic activity also occurred here and the mountain's summit mainly consists of andesitic lava, with some basalt flows, that later became encased within the granite because of cauldron subsidence.

The difference between the extrusive and intrusive rocks is best illustrated at the mountain's north face where the andesite forms immense crags soaring above the rounded granite of neighbouring Càrn Mòr Dearg, which is covered with vegetation almost to the top. During the last glacial period Ben Nevis'

summit remained ice-free, which explains its uneven character next to the ice-smoothed lower slopes. The two peaks are connected by the Càrn Mòr Dearg arête, considered by climbers to be the most technically demanding of the summit approaches; and together they encircle a glacial corrie that creates a natural amphitheatre of colossal proportions, the like of which is not seen elsewhere in the British Isles.

Ben Nevis stands 1,344m above sea level and is the chief in a horseshoe-shaped ridge of five peaks, all of which exceed 1,000m. It is, of course, the highest mountain in the British Isles (on land at least), and attracts over 100,000 visitors a year. The first documented ascent was by the botanist James Robertson in 1771, who was then followed by others including John Williams in 1774, who recorded a geological description of the mountain. Throughout this period Ben Nevis was in contest with Ben Macdui (1,309m), in the Cairngorms, for the title of highest mountain, but in 1847 the Ordnance Survey finally resolved the matter. During the nineteenth century the Victorian pioneers Raeburn, Collie and Naismith (of Naismith's rule) did much to popularize this mountain in particular and climbing as a sport in general.

43 The Devil's Point, Glen Dee, Cairngorms, Aberdeenshire

The most extensive manifestation of exposed Devonian granite is found in the Cairngorm mountain range, which has the distinction of being the highest and coldest plateau in the British Isles. The Cairngorms include five of Scotland's six tallest mountains and, although at 1,004m the Devil's Point is not among these, it nonetheless creates a strong impression. With its infernally sheer cliffs where a spur has been cut down to size by flowing ice, the peak thoroughly deserves its name Bod an Deamhain which delightfully translates as the Devil's Penis, later sanitised to 'point'. In spite of its distinct identity, it is in fact a subsidiary peak of Cairn Toul, which is 3km to the north and nearly 300m higher. In such close proximity to the Cairngorms' heartland, this spot is ideal to pause and assess the scale of what once stood here. These 1,000m plus peaks are merely the plutonic core of the Caledonian belt so it takes a mental leap, and much craning of the neck, to conceive how much further skyward these ancient mountains once soared.

The Cairngorm massif is a substantial barrier straddling parts of both Aberdeenshire and Perthshire, and throughout much of the central area it is so unaffected by human influence that it can be considered to be one of the last remaining truly wild parts of Britain. However, this does not mean that the mountains are inaccessible – in fact quite the opposite as they are intersected by several mountain passes including the u-shaped Lairig Ghru, a narrow glacial trough cut deep into the pink-orange granite (seen here disappearing into clouds). Along with neighbouring Carn a' Mhaim the Devil's Point guards the southern entrance to the pass near the place where the Geusachan Burn merges with the River Dee. The Lairig Ghru has long been an important route connecting The Forest of Mar, close to Braemar on the south side, with Rothiemurchus, near Aviemore to the north. In years gone by this provided a route for drovers who used it to take flocks from their Highland farms to Lowland markets.

44 The Cheviot from Easter Tor, Northumberland

Although Northumberland lies within England's borders, its northern reaches are an extension of Scottish-style topography, being a continuation of the Southern Upland terrane. Even though the Cheviot Hills cover a large area, at no point can they be considered an especially dramatic group of peaks. Even The Cheviot (at the middle of the image), at 815m the highest in the range, is simply a bigger bump among characteristically lumpy hills where exposures of rock are few and far between as they are largely hidden beneath blanket bog and heather. While the rounded scenery is explained by its igneous origin later shaped by ice, the unassuming appearance belies the momentous events that took place here. The Iapetus Suture zone runs right through the Cheviot Hills, dividing the scenery into distinct northern and southern parts. The north-eastern uplands were initially formed from explosively ejected frothy lava followed by less volatile outpourings of molten rock covering an area of 600km². In certain locations Cheviot Granite was later intruded deep within those rocks around 380 Ma and it is these plutons that form the area's highest summits.

Where rocks are revealed they create tors attesting to the variable nature of this landscape, as they could be either lava or granite. Some outcrops are easily identifiable as lava because of a particular feature called vesicles created when gases dissolved within the erupted magma escape as pressure decreases. Providing the rocks cool rapidly the bubbles remain suspended within them and form a pitted texture. If the magma is felsic it creates pumice, the rock that floats on water due to its low density, and which appears in many bathrooms thanks to its exfoliating properties. Easter Tor is composed from mafic scoria, which, although of similar appearance to pumice, does not float owing to the greater relative density of the iron it contains. Scoria consists of magma that was either at the surface of a lava flow, or possibly from melted fragments originating within a volcano.

DEVONIAN
419–359 Ma

45 Pen y Fan and Corn Du, Brecon Beacons, Powys

Throughout the Devonian the once mighty Caledonian Mountains weathered heavily and by the end of the period had nearly disappeared. However, sediments from the eroding range provided the new materials to build landforms on the Old Red Sandstone Continent (also known as Laurussia or Euramerica). This huge and exceptionally arid supercontinent was created by the merging of Avalonia-Baltica and Laurentia at a latitude thousands of kilometres south of the equator in the position now occupied by the Namibian Desert. The Old Red Sandstone (ORS) is named after the rusty-red colour of the oxidised iron that is an identifying feature of these rocks, and which indicates sediments laid down in dry lowlands either in lakes or river deltas, both of which are described as alluvial processes. However, not all rocks within the ORS group are so coloured but can be purple, green or dark brown, as some of the rocks are marine sediments laid down in shallow basins and contain greater amounts of mud and silt.

The sandstone, although named after deposits in Devon, is found at many sites across the country including the Brecon Beacons. Pen y Fan and Corn Du, the two highest mountains in South Wales, are formed from sandstone deposited in wide rivers and on coastal plains draining into the Rheic Ocean which stretched between the Old Red Sandstone continent and Gondwana. Both hills consist of three separate units of ORS and the distinctive flat summits are etched out of the hardest rock within the sequence, the Plateau Beds Formation. Pen y Fan's north-east face is a dramatic scalloped escarpment above a deep corrie or cwm, which in this case forms the head of a long valley. Together both peaks were formerly known as Cadair Arthur or 'Arthur's Seat' – a possible reference to King Arthur. The reason for the renaming is unclear, although Pen y Fan is at least topographically accurate as it translates from the Welsh as 'Top of this Place', whereas Corn Du is altogether more enigmatic as it means 'Dark Crib'.

46 Sugar Loaf (Pen-y-fal), Black Mountains, Monmouthshire

Named for its almost perfectly conical top, the Sugar Loaf is at the southern limit of the Black Mountains, also considered part of the Brecon Beacons, and although at 596m it is not especially high, it is instantly identifiable. The cone shape has led to it being mistaken for an extinct volcano, although the peak is of sedimentary origin and is mainly composed of the ORS found throughout the Brecon area and topped with quartz conglomerate formed from quartz pebbles that have become cemented together. The summit geology resists erosion far better than the underlying ORS so by comparison the surrounding mountains appear relatively flat.

During an excavation of an eighteenth-century settlement on the south-western slopes of the Sugar Loaf at the foothill Y Graig, an unexpected find was made. Flint tools were unearthed that dated from the Mesolithic, Neolithic and the Bronze Age, a period spanning from 10,000–1,000 BC. As the site was in use for 9,000 years it would suggest ancient peoples placed great importance on this landscape. Subsequent to the occupation of this site, an Iron Age hillfort was built on the adjacent Crug Hywel (Table Mountain) that is seen here, the flat top and steep sides of which made it the perfect choice for a defensive fort. The structure once occupied the entire hilltop although scattered rubble and earthern ramparts are now all that remain.

47 Carrauntoohil & Hag's Tooth, Macgillycuddy's Reeks, County Kerry

Two of Europe's notable mountain systems meet in Ireland: the older Caledonian belt to the north-west and the Devonian Armorican Highlands reaching from central Europe and through France before ending in southern Ireland. The latter are a series of ORS ridges, intersected by valleys that mainly outcrop in the far south of the country. Immediately south of the Dingle Peninsula (and south of the Variscan Front) the ORS forms an extensive mountain range known as Macgillycuddy's Reeks, which are named after the clan that owned the land. Alternately called the Black Stacks, they stretch across 19km and include twenty-four distinct summits, the highest of which Carrauntoohil – or Corrán Tuathail (Tuathal's Sickle) – rises to 1,038m, thus making it the highest peak in Ireland. The Armorican Highlands were created when a continental fragment rifted away from Gondwana in the late Silurian, and went on to collide with the ORS Continent as the Rheic Ocean closed at the end of the Carboniferous in an event known as the Variscan Orogeny (to be returned to later). The resulting impact thrust the older ORS northwards over the later Carboniferous limestone dominating central Ireland.

Unlike the ORS in the Brecon Beacons, these mountains have been eroded into pointed summits and include tors. One of them is The Hag's Tooth – also known as Stumpeenadaff (from Stuimpín an Daimh), meaning 'little pinnacle of the ox' – which sticks out from the mountainside at a quirky angle. The jagged forms attests to the mountains largely escaping the ice sheet that etched much of Britain and Ireland's landscape during the most recent glaciation. Instead of being buried under glacial ice, the land underwent periglacial conditions and was shaped by freeze-thaw cycles. During these events the upper layer of deposits slumped downhill as a result of soil fluction. This happens when sediments become waterlogged during a warmer episode and, as the underlying rocks are impermeable, anything above this barrier slips over the lubricated surface. During colder spells the erosion was accelerated by frost heave that occurred because frozen water expands, breaking apart saturated sediments as it does so. This process can easily be observed happening in a muddy or boggy environment on especially cold days when damp earth is prised open by growing ice crystals. As a result these peaks are buried under thick layers of silt and clay interspersed with rock fragments flowing across all but the craggiest of tors and sharpest of ridges.

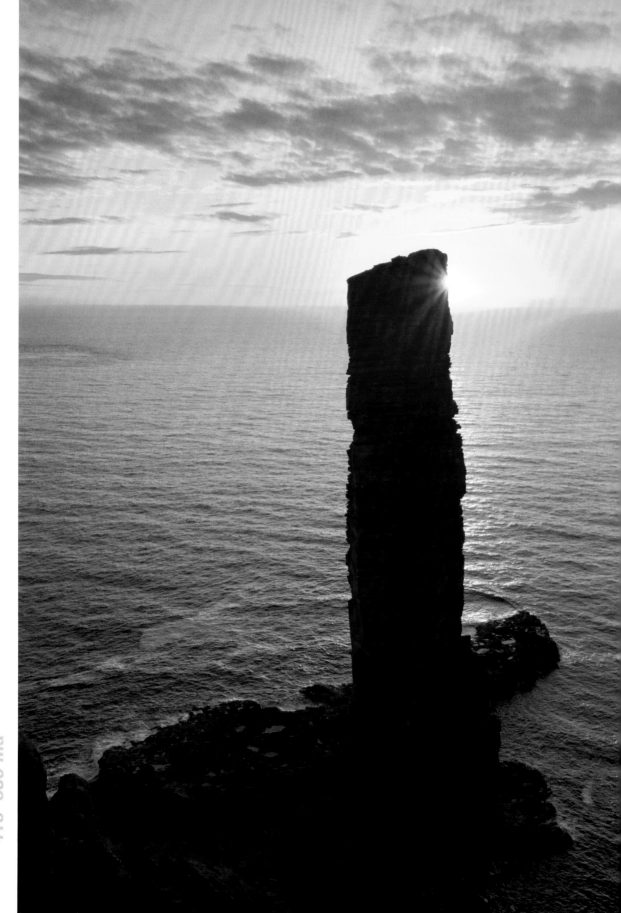

48 Old Man Of Hoy, Hoy, Orkney

The ORS is extensive throughout the Orkney Islands, where it forms rounded and sometimes craggy hills, the highest of which are on Hoy. This small island shows a strong contrast between the east and west coasts, the former low-lying and the latter dominated by high cliffs. Just to the north of Rackwick Bay lies the Old Man of Hoy, a 'finger-thin' sea stack reaching a vertigo-inducing 137m high, which is hewn from Middle and Upper Devonian ORS and perched on a base of wave-resistant basalt.

Maps made of the Orkney Islands between 1600 and 1750 do not feature the landform, although it is speculated to be 400 years old. An 1817 painting by William Daniell, which is in the Tate Gallery's collection, depicts the Old Man as a much wider column with an arch at the base. Over the last 200 years the stack's girth has been much diminished, and is showing signs that it may soon topple, which is not unexpected considering its vulnerability to Atlantic swell on all sides. A 40m crack runs vertically from the top of the stack so it will surely split apart, becoming narrower still, before completely wearing away and with it the memory of the coast's original outline.

Despite being formed from vivid iron-rich sandstone, the Old Man is as green as he is red due to a coating of algae and lichen. Slippery algae and bird guano add an extra degree of difficulty to would-be climbers so it was not until 1966 that the stack was first ascended. Chris Bonington, Rusty Baillie and Tom Patey led the successful team, taking three days to succeed. The following July the three men, accompanied by another three climbers, once again scaled the Old Man, only this time in front of a live audience of 15 million BBC television viewers. Both the climb and the broadcast were a triumph that helped consolidate the Old Man's fearsome reputation, arguably making it the most iconic sea stack in the British Isles.

49 Kynance Cove, The Lizard, Cornwall

The Lizard peninsula is the southernmost tip of Cornwall and of the British mainland. Kynance Cove is famed for its unusual serpentine (serpentinite) rock, coloured green or red and intruded with veins of other minerals, including lemon yellow soapstone. It was originally oceanic crust and upper mantle thought to date from around 400 Ma and, rather than being subducted back into the mantle in the usual manner, it has become attached to the main continental landmass. During this process the rocks have undergone low-temperature metamorphosis, reconfiguring the original peridotite. The serpentine did not arrive on land until the end of the Devonian when the northwards-moving Lizard Thrust, which occurred during the earliest phase of the Variscan Orogeny, pushed it into place.

These extremely rare formations, known as ophiolites, are the oldest examples of oceanic crust in existence as the rest is recycled every few hundred million years. As an exceptional example of this type of geology The Lizard peninsula is an internationally important site. The banded grey pebbles are schist and are associated with the same events that brought the serpentine into being although they have not undergone the same degree of deformation.

While it might be obvious to infer that The Lizard peninsula is named after the reptilian-looking rocks, this is not so. The area is named after the village of Lizard, which is thought to derive from the Cornish 'Lys Ardh', meaning 'high court'. Nonetheless the rock is synonymous with this landscape and is a financially important resource. Although this coastline once had a thriving fishing industry, it now relies on tourism as a major income source and the serpentine is carved into trinkets for selling in local shops.

50 Bedruthan Steps, Carnewas, Cornwall

The Carnewas cliffs are formed from metamorphosed sediments, mainly sandstone and shales from the Devonian and Carboniferous that were folded and faulted during the Variscan Orogeny at the end of the Carboniferous. The series of stacks represent sizeable chunks of cliff that have slipped into the sea and subsequently been shaped by Atlantic waves. The combination of sandstone and shale layers tends to be structurally weak because, as rainwater seeps between the alternating beds, the rocks become lubricated and the pressure applied by the weight of upper layers can cause slippage to occur.

There is an oft-cited legend of a giant who was credited with the creation of the stacks or 'steps'. However, this was a nineteenth-century invention and an early example of a marketing campaign aimed at attracting tourists. The 'steps' could refer to the stacks themselves or to the steep staircase cut into the rocks, which has been in place for at least 200 years. The effort required to cut these steps illustrates our collective determination to explore the locations that nature places tantalisingly just out of reach. Although officially closed during the 1960s and early 1970s due to a rock fall damaging the staircase, this did not prevent people from trying to descend to the beach. The National Trust has since restored access and secured the rocks with netting. The beach is notorious for the dangerous swell that arrives with the high tide but, despite this, it is still one of the most popular locations on the Cornish coast.

51 Arthur's Seat and Salisbury Crags, Edinburgh

In the early Carboniferous igneous activity in central Scotland's Midland Valley created Arthur's Seat, an extinct volcano the vent of which became plugged with hard-wearing basalt and agglomerates composed from large chunks of ejected rocks. The hill is the centrepiece of Holyrood Park where it rises fairly abruptly from a sedimentary plain to 251m above sea level, its presence dominating Edinburgh's skyline. The extent of the volcano can be traced through other landscape features, notably the granite pluton plugging one of the outlying vents 2km to the east of Arthur's Seat. This crag reaches 17m above Edinburgh's streets and is occupied by the city's castle. Some claim an Arthurian connection for the peak, as with Ben Arthur in the Arrochar Alps, although Sir William Maitland suggested that the name could well be a corruption of Ard-na-Said, meaning height of the arrows, implying that the hill had defensive significance.

There is no consensus as to the exact origin of the volcano. It could be that the Midland Valley formed as Britain was pulled towards the subduction zone at the north-western margin of the Old Red Sandstone continent. If so, Arthur's Seat is a rift-valley volcano where diverging plates opened up a fissure in the continental crust, allowing magma to seep up through a vent as happened at the mighty Kilimanjaro. Another possibility is that the continental plate drifted over a hot spot, a volcanic plume reaching up from the mantle, which can occur independently of or in conjunction with plate margins. A single hot spot created Hawaii's many islands because as the plate travelled slowly over the plume, magma was punched through the crust in separate bursts, almost like a dotted line. From the summit of Arthur's Seat it is possible to see two smaller volcanic plugs, North Berwick Law and Bass Rock, away to the northeast, which makes the hot spot theory credible. Ultimately, it could be a combination of the two, as seen on the exceptionally volcanic Iceland where the Eurasian and the North American Plates are drifting apart.

Below Arthur's Seat the dolerite Salisbury's Crag sill was squeezed between sandstone beds long after the volcano ceased to erupt. This stretch known as Hutton's Section was where the man himself suggested that the baking effect seen on the surrounding rocks, otherwise known as contact metamorphism, was evidence of its intrusive origin. Quarrying of the sill to pave Edinburgh's streets has much reduced its stature although it is still an impressive sight.

CARBONIFEROUS
359–299 Ma

52 Eildon Hills from Scott's View, Melrose, Berwickshire

Scott's View, so named because it was the favourite vista of Sir Walter Scott, overlooks a tight meander in the River Tweed that almost makes an island of Old Melrose, the site of the former Mailros Abbey founded by King Oswald in 635. The sweeping curve of wooded fields slopes up from the riverside and terminates in the three rounded summits that make up the Eildon Hills. The peaks, the highest of which is 422m, have a prominent relationship with the surrounding landscape, both in terms of physical presence and their shaping of local folklore. Formed from felstone (felsite), an intrusive igneous rock composed mainly from feldspar and quartz, the hills are a sill standing proud of the Old Red Sandstone country rock, which itself has weathered to form hilly scenery, none of which rivals the Eildons' stature. The landscape's contours are due to the weathering action of an ancient waterway much larger than the current river.

A less matter-of-fact version of events tells of a large hill split into a triptych through magical, or possibly even diabolical means, by Michael Scott, also known as the Borders Wizard, who was a philosopher to the court of the thirteenth century Holy Roman Empire. This is not the only tall tale associated with these hills. The laird and poet Thomas Learmount, better known as Thomas the Rhymer and born in nearby Earlstone, was a flesh-and-blood person around whom a fantastical narrative has been wrought. It is said that while out hunting Thomas dozed at the foot of the peaks, under Eildon Tree: woken by the Elvish Queen, she spirited him away to her kingdom inside the 'hollow' hills. He remained there for seven years, from where he returned to his own people for another seven before finally disappearing from the face of the Earth. It is supposed that he is once again under the hills and may yet return – a motif echoing the sleeping King Arthur and his Knights at Long Mynd. The spot where the supernatural encounter took place is now marked by The Rhymer's Stone, which was erected by the Melrose Literary Society in 1929.

53 Mewslade Bay, Pitton, Gower

In the early part of the Carboniferous period, Britain and Ireland were positioned at the equator and submerged under the warm shallows of the Rheic Ocean that had arrived from the south towards the end of the Devonian. As the hard-shelled sea creatures populating these tropical waters died, and their calcium carbonate rich remains settled on the sea floor, beds of limestone were formed. South Wales has large areas of limestone, and where it meets the sea there are some spectacular cliffs. These towers at Mewslade Bay on Gower Peninsula are layers folded into an upright position and split along the bedding plane, an example of which can be seen running diagonally across the cliff's base. This movement occurred during the Variscan Orogeny around 280 Ma that, unlike the earlier Caledonian Orogeny, did not create any equivalent-sized mountains in Britain or Ireland. Instead it substantially deformed many rocks in the southern parts of the British Isles.

As these cliffs are largely underwater at high tide, they suffer extensive wave erosion that carves out many small caves among the strangely textured rocks. These cliffs are so unusual that they would not look out of place on another planet. This is the domain of gregarious seabirds that turn the peculiarly etched niches into safe nesting sites, so it is these feathered-residents that give Mewslade Bay its title. Mew Gull is another name for the Common Gull so familiar to our coastal cliffs, and slade or 'slaed' is from the Old English for valley, making this the Valley of the Gulls.

54 Winnats Pass, Castleton, Hope Valley, Derbyshire

Winnats Pass is a deep and steep-sided ravine cut through a coral reef that grew in warm shallow seas around 350 Ma. However, for many years the landform was thought to be a cave system with a collapsed roof, which is not an unreasonable assumption as Castleton has no fewer than four separate cave systems, one of which lies right at the foot of the pass. Reefs have been around in one form or another throughout the history of life on Earth, and make a significant contribution to the global distribution of limestone.

Derbyshire's White Peak area is famous for its exceptionally pure limestone and its pale colour is referenced in the region's name. As the rock is 98 per cent calcium carbonate, it is an indispensable resource for many industries. Blocks of it are used for building, and its heated and powdered form, lime, is a key ingredient in cement and is used as a flux for smelting iron. Also known as 'quicklime', it is used to make alkaline fertilisers for improving soil condition and there is a long history of lime production in Britain,

with evidence indicating that the practice was common from the Roman period onwards. The remains of post-Roman limekilns are familiar feature throughout the White Peak's landscape. The limestone also provided material for drystone walls running all the way along the precipitous upper edges of the ravine, as not a scrap of land was left unclaimed when previously common grazing areas began to be formally divided up in the Middle Ages, and became legally defined by Parliamentary Enclosure Acts in the eighteenth and nineteenth centuries.

The road heading up the pass is wide enough for two cars in most places, which gives some idea of the ravine's impressive scale. This is the only route west out of Castleton but due to the 1:5 gradient it is often impassable during bad winter weather conditions. The name Winnats is a corruption of 'Windygates' and refers to the effects of the powerful easterly wind as it is channelled up the ravine and around the rock pinnacles that define the upper reaches.

55 Cheddar Gorge, Somerset

Cheddar Gorge runs through the north-western part of the Mendip Hills, which are Britain's most southerly example of Carboniferous limestone uplands. The hills are an anticline overlooking the flat-as-a-pancake coastal plains and wetlands that make up the Somerset Levels and Moors. The geographical prominence explains the name Cheddar, which, like the Welsh *cadair*, means 'chair'. The long-winding gorge is the largest of its type in the British Isles and was created by a deluge of glacial meltwaters passing through Somerset en route to the sea. Today there is no surface river, as it has long since vanished. However, the underground Cheddar Yeo River reappears in Gough's Cave. The gorge is a classic example of a karst landscape where the soluble limestone is slowly eaten away by rainwater. As rain falls it captures carbon dioxide from the atmosphere and forms carbonic acid which, although only weakly acidic, is enough, given time and the abrasive action of loose rock fragments

caught up in the flow, to carve out extensive subterranean chambers.

The human relationship with Cheddar stretches back far into prehistory with traces of habitation of its many caves dating back 40,000 years. This means that our ancestors sheltered here in the millennia leading up to the Last Glacial Maximum (26,000–19,000 years ago), when an ice sheet reached from the North Pole as far south as Birmingham. Excavations in Gough's Cave revealed the oldest complete human skeleton found in Britain, known as Cheddar Man, dated to 9,000 years old. Gruesomely butchered human remains were also discovered that date from around 14,700 years ago. Rather than deliberate killing this is thought to be an example of where those who had died from natural causes were eaten because food was so scarce. Intriguingly some skulls had been turned into what appear to be drinking cups that could have been for either practical or ritual purposes.

56 Benbulbin/Ben Bulben, Drumcliffe, County Sligo

This immense landform was originally a conventional ridge at the edge of a raised plateau, since sliced and sculpted by glaciers to resemble a table-top mountain reaching 526m high. The steep upper parts are composed of Dartry Limestone resting on Glencar Limestone, while the smooth sides consist of Benbulben Shale that is largely vegetated and partly hidden by scree dislodged from higher up. The tough upper beds have provided a protective cap for the less resistant lower layers, and differential weathering has created the extraordinary appearance best described as half hill, half cliff. Erosion scars from rainwater run-off take the form of deeply-set gullies big enough to be visible from Streedagh Point over 5km away. Benbulbin's north-western face looks like a kilometre-long wall standing separately from the adjacent hill. However, appearances are deceptive as, when viewed from the west, the peak comes to an angular point clearly connected to Kings Mountain, and together they are only the tip of the Dartry Mountain Range. It is from this angle that the Gaelic name Binn Ghulbain makes sense, as it is said to mean jaw-shaped peak, although not everyone agrees with this interpretation because Ghulbain could be a proper noun rather than an adjective.

CARBONIFEROUS
359–299 Ma

The area around Benbulbin is known as Yeats Country, after the celebrated poet W.B. Yeats, who grew up in the nearby town of Sligo. In 'Under Ben Bulben', he describes his final resting place in Drumcliffe churchyard and that is indeed where he is buried. He could not have chosen a better spot from which to take in the hill for all eternity.

That such a prominent landform should figure repeatedly in Irish writing is no surprise and it is also the setting for *The Pursuit of Diarmuid and Gráinne*, a mythological narrative with tenth-century origins. In this tale, a love triangle existed between Fionn mac Cumhaill, the leader of the Fianna – a legendary band of warriors – the princess Gráinne, and her love Diarmuid Ua Duibhne, also a member of the Fianna. In a fit of jealousy Fionn tricked Diarmuid into hunting an enchanted boar on land below Benbulbin, where the creature mortally wounded Diarmuid, piercing him through the heart with its tusk. Fionn, also known as Finn McCool, is linked with other Celtic sites and will reappear later in this book.

57 Malham Cove, Malham, North Yorkshire

Malham Cove has an overpowering presence because of the 80m high and 300m wide horseshoe-shaped cliff formed from limestone beds tilted upwards when the rocks below slipped down the Craven Mid Fault. Rivers sometimes cut through rocks and at other times they spread out across the surface to create broad waterfalls. During the periodic thaws of the last glaciation, meltwaters poured over the cliff edge in a huge cascade that eroded the limestone backwards up the valley. At the flow's centre a deep groove was cut and once this process was underway, it channelled the waterfall so that greater erosion occurred at this point, creating the classic curving cove structure. It is hard to gain a sense of what great deluges these cyclical floods produced, although the scale is hinted at as it is known that the original cliffs were 600m further down the valley, and would have ended where Malham village begins.

As the ice finally relaxed its grip, the ancient river disappeared underground through the porous rock creating the limestone pavement formation (see next page) that covers the cliff's upper surface. Underground rivers and pavements often occur together as both are examples of karst erosion. It was long assumed that what remains of this ancient river, the Malham Tarn glacial lake about 2km to the north, is the source of the stream that emerges from the base of Malham Cove's cliffs. However, after tests it was discovered that Malham Beck's origin is away to the north-west, where a stream running from the sides of Black Hill darts underground through water-worn channels and caves before reappearing 2km away trickling from a gap at the bottom of the cove.

58 Knockanes, The Burren, County Clare

Limestone pavements are among the world's more unusual landscape features and are shaped by both ice and water. Initially formed by the scouring action of glaciers which, as they advance, remove overlying loose sediments to reveal horizontal limestone beds and, when they retreat, the rock is scraped completely flat. Then rainwater finds lines of weakness within the rock, a process that eventually dissolves enough material for deep fissures or 'grikes' to open up, leaving slabs or 'clints' that can have a surprisingly regular pavement-like appearance. The Knockanes ridge's horizontal uniformity is subverted by sweeping curved terraces, which, seen from a satellite view, exactly imitate map contour lines. This results from the erosion of both anticlinal and synclinal folding that took place during the Variscan Orogeny. It is strange that these natural upheavals should create a scene that at a glance so resembles the tiered workings of a quarry, a frequent feature of limestone areas.

The Burren covers 250km² of Ireland's central terrane, or 1 per cent of the country's total landmass, making it the most significant glacio-karst landscape in Western Europe. Ireland has a total of 360km² of pavement, which is more than ten times the area found throughout the whole of Britain. Burren comes from *boireann*, meaning rocky place, and while this is apt for this apparently barren landscape, where there is soil it is fertile and the grikes offer shelter to a broad variety of plants (detail on page 13). This extraordinary ecosystem has alpines usually found in the Arctic living next to Mediterranean plants. The Burren would not be half of what it is today without the positive influence of generations of farmers. Their land management techniques have been sympathetic to the area's natural diversity and have encouraged the habitat to thrive.

Despite their status as globally important habitats, not all limestone pavements have fared so well. Valued for its sculptural appearance, it is a popular stone for garden ornamentation. Large-scale mechanised quarrying of pavements began in the mid-twentieth century and carried on until the 1980s, when legislation was passed in the UK to protect them. Now there is only one quarry left in Britain with permission to extract it, but many sites in Ireland are not protected and could be at risk. Rocks from limestone pavements are still for sale in garden centres, some from Britain and Ireland, but mostly from overseas. It is hard to understand, in our supposedly more enlightened times, how it is lawful wilfully to cause such ecological vandalism in the pursuit of gardening.

59 Twisleton Scars and Whernside, near Ingleton, North Yorkshire ⇒

In Yorkshire where most of England's limestone pavements are found, and throughout northern Britain, these landforms are known as 'scars'. This evocative expression perfectly describes their riven and fragmented character. A regular addition to pavements throughout Britain and Ireland are erratic boulders deposited in the wake of the retreating ice. At Twisleton these large boulders are limestone originating from elsewhere on the plateau. Whereas at nearby Norber the erratics are Jurassic sandstone that is younger, and has travelled much further, to end up on top of Carboniferous strata.

The Carboniferous Limestone forms part of the Pennine mountain chain running north–south through the middle of northern England, separating northwest from north-east. The other major element of the Pennines is Millstone Grit, which is a coarse, late Carboniferous sandstone consisting of grit and sand transported via river deltas from eroding northern uplands and deposited in the marine Pennine Basin beginning around 320 Ma. These sediments spread out over much of the older limestone and together they were folded into anticlines and synclines during the Variscan Orogeny, although by the time its effects had reached this far north some of its force had been reduced, much like dissipating pond ripples. The alternating sequence of folds explains the deep valleys and high ridges that typify the Pennine landscape.

The Millstone Grit typically forms escarpments and angular hills such as Whernside, which at 736m is the loftiest of Yorkshire's Three Peaks and is the highest point in the county. The Cumbrian border runs through Whernside's middle; however, it is well down the list of that region's highest mountains. 'Whern' is believed to derive from quernstone, a type of hand-operated rotary millstone used for grinding grain that was introduced into Britain during the Iron Age, suggesting that the peak was recognised as a useful source of this rock. The Millstone Grit is so named because it was a favourite material for making millstones. However, it had the unfortunate side-effect of turning the flour grey with fine traces of rock, which predictably had damaging effects on teeth.

60 Stanage Edge, Hathersage, Derbyshire

At over 6km, Stanage Edge is the longest inland escarpment in England and it is impossible to appreciate its full extent from any one position. It is at the southern limit of the Pennine range and is formed from Millstone Grit where rounded river-tumbled quartz pebbles are seen protruding from the surface. The rock shows noticeable cross-bedding, where layers within the beds are inclined on an angle rather than being horizontal (see page 10: Red Rock, Pease Bay). Where ripples form on a riverbed the downstream current continuously washes sediments over the top of them. Some of these sediments clump together at the ripple's crest until the weight becomes so great that they fall down the leeward side, creating a sloping bed that is steep compared to the more gently inclined ripple. As this process repeats, sets of cross-beds are formed that are consistent in both angle and direction, until conditions change and a new set begins. An equivalent process happens in deserts where the wind transports sand grains over the top of dunes.

This type of sandstone has few lines of weakness, which makes it ideal for carving into millstones as it can be cut along any plane within the rock. This once-important industry employed many people in the north Derbyshire region during the seventeenth and eighteenth centuries. Now only occasional millstones scattered across the moors among tumbled rocks, brackens and heather are left as reminders. Several examples can be seen directly below this escarpment, some of which are apparently finished while others were abandoned partway through the carving process.

The word Stanage is a corruption of 'stone edge' so in effect it is named twice over, which is why locals (including myself) refer to it simply as Stanage. Today the escarpment is a magnet for rock-climbers as its weathered joints along the inclined bedding are exceptionally 'well-designed' for jamming hands and feet into, and the gritty texture provides a tactile surface with good grip. Stanage's reputation means that it is one of the most popular climbing destinations in the country and it is often crawling with people on fine evenings and at weekends. From a distance the dozens of people dangling from ropes along the dark rocks look like so many colourful ants dwarfed by the edge's enormous scale.

CARBONIFEROUS
359–299 Ma

61 Cliffs of Moher, Lislorkan North, County Clare

In the late Carboniferous period the sea level rose, and limestone basins were filled in with sand and mud washed down river deltas from high ground during floods – an example of a fluvial process. This created alternating beds of sandstone, shale and siltstone, a rock-like sandstone consisting of smaller grains that, as the name implies, is mainly silt rather than clay based. Between floods, current ripples developed on the floor of a calm sea, as can be seen forming on any sandy beach, and are accompanied by tracks created by snails or woodlouse-like creatures. These trace-fossils were preserved by fine sediments settling over the top of them and are a recurrent feature of Moher's sandstones.

The Cliffs of Moher are the most impressive Carboniferous sandstone sea cliffs in Ireland and, arguably, the whole of the British Isles. Extending for 8km along the Burren's southwestern edge and facing the unquiet Atlantic, there is nothing west of this point until land is reached at Newfoundland 3,000km away. This 7km stretch snakes all the way to Hag's Head, the cliffs taking their name from a rock formation said to resemble the mythological Old Hag figure (who will be returned to later). Rising as high as 214m, the cliffs are visually stunning which explains why they draw in over 1 million visitors a year, making them one of Ireland's most visited natural attractions, and ensuring their inclusion in the Burren and Cliffs of Moher Geopark.

In this 170m-high section the different phases of fluvial deposition are clearly visible and, once again, the combination of alternating sandstone, shale and siltstone strata is worryingly unstable. The foreground consists of shales that have been split into small fragments, due to the advanced state of weathering, and capped with friable boulder clay left behind by a retreating glacier. Immediately below this is a large sandstone slab, easily distinguishable from the rounded shale by its angular corners, which has also been severely curtailed by erosion. A path runs along the cliff as far as the eye can see, although parts of it are now off-limits as it is just a few centimetres away from the crumbling edge.

62 Alport Castles, Alport Dale, Derbyshire

Alport Dale lies at the base of the Pennine range rather in the shadow of the adjacent Kinder Scout, a mountain plateau that is the high point of the Peak District. This terraced escarpment runs along the valley's eastern perimeter, and its elevation and composition of alternating layers of sandstone and shale make it appear fortress-like and well deserving of the Alport Castles name. The unstable beds resulted in a landslip where a great mass of material slumping down the hillside affected a large area. Where it came to rest several mounds were created, the largest of which is the 'The Tower', a name that refers to its similarity to a 'motte and bailey' type castle.

Although the landscape may currently appear static, slips can happen at any time, particularly after prolonged periods of heavy rain. While this poses less of a problem in remote locations such as Alport Dale, unless you happen to live in the farm below this spot, in 2008 the A57 Snake Pass route between Sheffield to Manchester – 2km to the south – was closed owing to hillside movements causing sizeable gaps in the road. A recent journey along the pass revealed that the land is once again on the move, with fresh cracks showing in the tarmac. A landslide affecting similar strata at Mam Tor, also known as the 'Shivering Mountain' – at Castleton to the south of Kinder Scout – caused the main A625 Sheffield to Manchester road to be closed permanently in 1979 after repeated attempts to reconstruct it. This section of the road was rerouted through the comparatively stable limestone of Winnats Pass.

CARBONIFEROUS
359–299 Ma

63 Brimham Rocks, Nidderdale, North Yorkshire

Brimham Moor is renowned for its extraordinary Millstone Grit outcrops, none of which is more curious than the 'balanced' rocks such as this one called the Idol Rock. These are not erratics transported from elsewhere, as might initially be supposed, rather these tors were fashioned from the surrounding rock, indicating the former extent and height of the escarpment. The feldspar within this type of sandstone is especially susceptible to chemical weathering by rainwater. When water passes through the permeable rock, the feldspar's ions are dissolved and the mineral is transformed into friable clay that is easily broken down by mechanical weathering by wind and abrasive rock particles. At the end of the most recent glaciation, the thin ice covering Brimham Moor melted as temperatures began to rise, and the exposed rocks were sandblasted by windblown ice crystals combined with sharp grains from other eroded rocks. These effects were concentrated at ground level and this has meant that the underside of tors has largely been eaten away leaving only a narrow plinth of resistant rock to support tonnes of weight.

All manner of folklore is ascribed to these unusual formations, which were once thought to be man-made, and some hints of these legends are immortalised in their evocative names. Near to the Idol Rock is the Druid's Writing Desk, which was allegedly carved as a ceremonial feature. While it is easy to imagine that such a fantastic landform could become the focus of ritual activity, it is unlikely that it had anything do with Druids. Mother Shipton, of the famous limestone petrifying well at nearby Knaresborough, makes an appearance among the 'human' shaped tors and other simulacrum are said to resemble a sphinx and a dancing bear.

64 Millook Haven, Cornwall

The Killas, named by local miners, is a Cornish term for the slate/phyllite underlying two-thirds of the county. The first deposits date from the Devonian but those in north Cornwall, such as here at Millook Haven, are Carboniferous. The metamorphism took place not long after the beds were laid down, and was caused by intense folding and deformation during the Variscan Orogeny. As the African plate drifted northwards into the European plate the Rheic Ocean closed and many fold mountains, including the Pyrenees, formed along the suture zone. However, none was created within the British Isles: instead the evidence of this event in Britain and Ireland is demonstrated through folded and deformed rocks. By the close of the Carboniferous, all land had coalesced into the single supercontinent Pangaea surrounded by the superocean Panthalassa, the former meaning 'entire Earth' and the latter 'entire sea', as labelled by Alfred Wegener, the pioneer of continental drift theory.

Millook Haven's zig-zag cliffs exhibit an extreme example of folding, and this particular variation, known as chevron folding, is associated with rocks laid down in a rapidly alternating sequence, for example, sandstone interleaved with shale. While many rocks demonstrate curved folds, alternating sediments have structural differences and this makes them prone to producing exceptionally tight folds, showing an acute angle at the 'hinge' and entirely straight 'limbs'. That it should do this is a little surprising as rocks behave fluidly during the deformation process, and curved folds are the most logical outcome. However, imagine a series of tightly-packed layers which, put under sideways pressure, start to bend upwards, and because the beds remain parallel gaps open up between the peaks and troughs of each fold. Nature does not tolerate inefficient use of space and will collapse these voids by tightening the hinge and straightening the limbs, creating zig-zag layers that perfectly align from one to the next.

65 Haytor, Haytor Vale, Devon

Haytor is a granite outcrop that is an exposed portion of a batholith, a huge mass of plutonic rock underlying much of Devon and Cornwall. The molten rock was intruded into fissures within Devonian and Carboniferous beds and, when the country rocks were eventually worn away, the granite was revealed across the high ground of both counties, most famously at Bodmin Moor and Dartmoor. As the granite cooled, dissolved metals contained within the magma were injected under great pressure into the surrounding rocks, and this created mineral deposits such as tin and copper, for which Cornwall is especially well known.

The outcrop occupies a prominent position on the eastern edge of Dartmoor and takes its name from this fact, as it was previously called 'Hey Tor' from *heah*, meaning high. It is of a type known as an 'avenue tor', where erosion of intervening rocks has divided a single outcrop in two. Dartmoor's geomorphology has long been considered the result of frost shattering, rather than abrasion by ice, as it was thought that the ice sheet did not reach this far south during the Quaternary Ice Age. However, this idea has been contradicted by recent evidence supporting the presence of a separate 100m thick icecap covering up to $80km^2$.

Haytor is the archetypal landform symbolising the area, which has led to it being incorporated within the design of the National Park logo. It is for the most part an easy climb as in the nineteenth century steps were carved into its flank (on other side of what is seen here) and a metal rail was attached, rusted traces of which remain. Haytor is only one of a long list of rocks modified to make ascending them easier. Scaling Haytor now seems like a hollow ritual as the challenge inspiring the desire to climb rocks in the first place has been tamed.

PERMIAN
299–253 Ma

66 Cheesewring Tor, Minions, Bodmin Moor, Cornwall

Stowe Hill has numerous distinctive granite formations although they all pale into insignificance when compared with the enigmatic Cheesewring Tor, the structure of which defies belief. Reaching over 7m high the balancing act looks far too precarious and yet it still stands. Gravity may yet win the battle however, as a close look at the narrow column reveals the presence of three metal rods holding the rocks in place, without which the tor would surely tumble. It says much about the way we interact with the landscape that an intervention has been made to 'fix' the formation at a precise point in time. Cheesewring Tor is not alone in its cultural value having to accord to an idealised shape in perpetuity rather than succumb to natural processes.

Although the strange appearance, likened to a stack of round cheeses, is a result of extreme weathering, in Cornish legend the arrangement was attributed to giants. In an interesting variation on the well established theme, the tor was alleged to be the result of a stone throwing competition between the local giant Uther and the recently arrived St Tue who, along with other early Christians, was busy spreading the new religion and claiming natural springs as holy wells. This upset Uther, who believed that the land, and all that it contained, belonged to him and the other giants and so the challenge was set. Owing to divine intervention he unexpectedly lost the competition and was obliged to make way for Christianity's spread throughout Cornwall. It is clear that this landscape was sacred to late Neolithic and early Bronze Age peoples, as metres away from Stowe Hill they erected the three stone circles collectively known as The Hurlers. The Hurlers' mythology also recalls tension between pagan and Christian practices, as the circles are reputed to be groups of men and women turned to stone for the sin of playing the hurling ball game on the Sabbath.

67 Great Whin Sill, Bamburgh, Northumberland ⇒

Like many castles before and since, the one at Bamburgh takes advantage of an easily defended sheer-sided rock outcrop. Since the last glaciation, large sand dunes have gathered against the rock and partly submerged it, but even so it is still an imposing crag. The castle is built on part of the Great Whin Sill, a group of dolerite intrusions extending throughout Northumberland and County Durham that date from the late Carboniferous and early Permian periods. At this location the dolerite was squeezed between Carboniferous limestone beds, which have weathered away to leave the sill standing proud. The name derives from whinstone, which is a generic quarrying term for igneous rocks, including basalt and dolerite that are so hard they do not split readily when struck with a pick.

Harkess Rocks, found 1km along the shore from the castle, are also part of the sill. Taking the shape of tiered platforms with angular edges, they emerge where waves have washed away the covering sands. A little way out to sea, the sill appears again as the group of low-lying rocks making up the Farne Islands. Further up the coast to the north-west the dolerite forms Holy Island, home to Lindisfarne Abbey, while to the south-east it underlies Dunstanburgh Castle and creates the distinctive cannonball shaped boulders of Embleton Bay. However, by far the largest continuous section of the Great Whin Sill protrudes in an east–west alignment across much of north Northumberland and into Cumbria. Its natural potential was realised by the ingenious Romans, who put it to use as the foundation for Hadrian's Wall.

68 High Cup Nick, Dufton, Cumbria

High Cup Nick lies at the head of a horseshoe-shaped dolerite amphitheatre that assumes the familiar columnar form readily distinguishing it from other rocks. The crags are a continuation of the Great Whin Sill and, in common with Bamburgh, the magma was intruded into Carboniferous limestone beds. These sediments have since been stripped back to leave a long and wide valley fringed with dramatic pinnacles that define the edge of the dolerite expanse of High Cup Plain. Even at its lowest point the plateau is a lofty 560m above sea level and is a significant water-catchment area riddled with tributaries, springs and pools. A stream, sometimes producing a small waterfall when the weather is wet enough, intersects the valley head. This trickle is a mere trace of the ancient river that bit so deeply into the limestone before slowly taking on the tougher dolerite.

The magma forming the Great Whin Sill flowed southwards from the area around Arthur's Seat and is roughly contemporary with the development of the Salisbury Crags. Like basalt, dolerite flows freely and it forms in chambers between 2–5km beneath the earth's surface – as such it is classed as subvolcanic. The insulating effect of the surrounding rocks means that dolerite remains molten for many thousands of years so is capable of travelling great distances, in this case over 200km from the source at Edinburgh. The thicker the intrusion the longer it takes to solidify, and a sill 1km in depth will take approximately 8,000 years to cool completely.

It is a convention that when 'Nick' appears in a place name it is usually a reference to Old Nick: the Devil. This attribution is certainly apt for this strange landscape, which can be outright eerie when the clouds come down. Looking back along the beck and the 4km route along which one walks, odd feelings of awe and isolation take over in this unique place of gigantic proportions resembling nothing else within the British Isles.

PERMIAN
299–253 Ma

69 Merkland Point, Isle of Arran

In Britain the Permian and subsequent Triassic periods are dominated by New Red Sandstone rocks. These form much of the east coast of Arran, an island that is at the western limit of the Midland Valley terrane. As with the Devonian Old Red Sandstone that preceded it, the startlingly red pigmentation is caused by rusting, indicating that these sediments were deposited in a dry environment. From the late Carboniferous Britain and Ireland consisted of a highland area locked inside Pangaea, with a desert climate persisting for 30 million years. Consequently these rocks are sand dunes almost entirely composed of quartz crystals cemented together with ferric iron oxide (haematite), other minerals being rarities. Aeolian processes (so named after the Greek god Aeolus, who was the keeper of winds) shaped the dunes and wind, often carrying abrasive sand grains, is the primary erosive force in desert environments.

Merkland Point's rocks have a peculiarly textured surface where many narrow quartz veins protrude from the host sandstone, some of which stand out tens of centimetres while others merely millimetres. The quartz veins have eroded more slowly as they are harder-wearing than the surrounding rock. These seams often run for metres at a time and produce an effect slightly reminiscent of the lines on the palm of one's hand. Grey granite erratics of a later date are scattered along the foreshore having been transported from the island's mountainous interior (which will be discussed later) by glaciers occurring around 15,000 years ago and then moved into their final resting places by mudflows.

70 Langstone Rock, Dawlish, Devon

The Dawlish Sandstone is found west of the Exmouth estuary and is just one of the named units making up Devon's striking red cliffs. A noticeable transition can be seen here between a band of Exe Breccia (at the bottom), composed of rubble and sediments brought down from higher ground to the west during flash floods, and the finer grained Dawlish Sandstone that, in common with other Permian New Red Sandstones, are aeolian-formed dunes. The breccia is a primarily loosely consolidated rock and it is possible, though not advisable, to extract exposed pebbles manually from the slightly sticky matrix. The sandstone displays cross-bedding where the crest of an older dune has been partially eroded away then buried under more encroaching sands, a cycle which has been repeated many times.

The combined strata is inherently weak and this proved to be an advantage to railway engineers who turned what was once Langstone Point, and very much part of the cliffs, into Langstone Rock, when they dug a railway cutting behind it. Wherever there is a weakness to be exploited along a joint in the rock there is the beginnings of a cave, and the arch illustrates the latter stages of this erosion process. The sea comes at it from the south-west, where the sandy beach is anchored by a breakwater, and also from an easterly direction. Despite the breakwater, Langstone Rock's south-east corner is still vulnerable to the waves so the base of the arch base is reinforced with boards banked up with sand to stop the sea pouring through from behind. This is a hybrid landform and an experiment with unstable rock that will inevitably end with the arch collapsing to form a pillar. No one knows how long this will take and what will have happened to the rest of the railway line meanwhile. The track is set back just a few metres from this spot along a platform not far above sea level at high tide. It provides an illusion of comparative safety at least until the next violent storm.

71 Lot's Wife, Marsden Bay, South Tyneside

After the sustained drought of the early Permian, the later epochs saw much of Britain and Ireland underwater, resulting from polar ice melt, an event that created the Tethys Ocean and the Zechstein Sea, separated from the main ocean by low banks. The shallow sea periodically evaporated and because the waters were rich in potassium salts and halites (rock salt), they left beds of gypsum and anhydrite in their wake, which formed crystal encrusted salt pans. The Earth's crust rose and fell periodically, allowing the ocean to break the barriers and replenish the sea, creating layers of sediments alternating with salt deposits. Ultimately the warm climate ensured that the Zechstein Sea had completely vanished by the end of the period. Permian salt deposits extend across northern England and into Central Europe. Many sites are worked commercially, some of which have a history of extraction dating back 7,000 years.

At Marsden Bay these salt pans were deposited in conjunction with dolomite beds. On exposure to the elements the saline deposits dissolved out from between the dolomite layers causing the strata to collapse, leaving densely packed beds with obvious jointing best seen in the bay's wave-ravaged stacks. One of the stacks is called Lot's Wife and when named it was not known how apt it was, as it refers to the form rather than the composition. The biblical character Lot's Wife was turned into a pillar of salt as punishment for looking back on Sodom and Gomorrah's fiery destruction, although specifically instructed not to.

The Permian period was brought to an apocalyptic end with the Permian–Triassic extinction event which was the worst the Earth has ever experienced. Also known as the Great Dying because as much as 96 per cent of marine and 70 per cent of terrestrial organisms were wiped out. It occurred in pulses the earliest of which was due to climatic changes, although later stages are variously ascribed to multiple meteorite impacts, an increase in volcanic activity and massive releases of methane from cracks in the seabed. The event defined the end of the Palaeozoic Era and the beginning of the Mesozoic Era (Greek: 'middle life').

72 Ladram Bay, Otterton, Devon

Further east along the coast from Langstone Rock at Dawlish, and moving forward one geological period, is the red Otter Sandstone at Ladram Bay. The rock occurs most dramatically in coastal cliff exposures, although the character- istic pigment colours the local soil and is especially noticeable in the agricultural landscape. Unlike the Dawlish Sandstone, these rocks are fluvial deposits carried downriver from what remained of the European Variscan uplands and laid down across a desert floodplain. Far from being a barren expanse, ripple and channel marks within the rock along with fossil- ised plants and animals, including fish, indicate that this desert supported fertile rivers. Of particular note are the Triassic reptile fossils within the Otter Sandstone, which are some of the best in the world. In common with all New Red Sandstones, Ladram Bay's rocks are relatively soft so it is only because this stack is rooted on a base of harder sandstone that has stopped it, and the other ones in the bay, from entirely disappearing.

Ladram Bay is part of a sequence of locations included in the Dorset and East Devon Coast UNESCO World Heritage Site, which between them span an inter- val of roughly 185 million years and three geological periods. Despite the fact that this stretch encompasses rocks from the Triassic, the Jurassic and the Cretaceous, it is popularly referred to as simply the Jurassic Coast. The designa- tion covers a 150km section of coastline from Orcombe Point at Exmouth in the west to Old Harry Rocks at Studland in the east, and shows a broad collection of sedimentary rocks. The oldest beds are the sandstones found at the western end, which progress to the youngest, the Cretaceous chalks, in the east.

TRIASSIC
253–201 Ma

73 Holy Austin Rock, Kinver Edge, Staffordshire

Throughout prehistory, humans have taken advantage of the shelter offered by caves, although most of this occupation was the opportunistic exploitation of pre-existing features with little modification. However, where rocks readily yield to tools, would-be troglodytes have carved out living spaces that usually follow natural fissures along joints. Cave houses are frequently basic in design but the red rocks of Kinver Edge boast some surprising additions. In places, the escarpment has become a man-made jumble of windows and doors set into weathered sandstone, punctuated by bricks and embellished with whitewash.

The Holy Austin rock houses, named after a local hermit, were still occupied in the 1950s, at which point they were declared unfit for habitation, making them the last known cave dwellings in Britain. Once vacant, the decay set in with cracks opening up and tree roots undermining structural stability. During the 1990s, the National Trust, which owns the properties, undertook extensive restoration work, including returning one of the cottage interiors to its Victorian heyday. These bijou homes with their neat little gardens are national treasures and are reputed to have inspired J.R.R. Tolkein, certainly evoking shades of Hobbiton.

The friable sandstone is an obvious target for graffiti, as the softer the rock the bigger the temptation. It is human nature to carve an identifying mark or to daub paint wherever there is a blank canvas. Aerosols are to concrete as tools are to rock, and the chosen method reflects the environment – be it urban or rural. Whether this is dismissed as vandalism or celebrated as art is a question of context and historical perspective.

74 Nash Point, Marcross, Glamorgan

The rifting that began the break-up of Pangaea in the Triassic continued apace in the Jurassic, splitting the supercontinent into northern and southern parts: Laurasia and Gondwana respectively, divided by the growing Tethys Ocean. This fragmentation presaged the distribution of continents that we are familiar with today. Continental drift caused sea levels to rise and much of Britain was submerged under a warm equatorial sea, which initiated a phase of marine sediment deposition across England stretching from the Cleveland Hills in Yorkshire to the Dorset coast, with a further small occurrence here in South Wales.

Nash Point is a distinctive headland located on the Glamorgan Heritage Coast and is part of a series of cliffs defining the Bristol Channel's northern shore. The cliffs are beds of rapidly alternating Liassic (layered) limestone and shale, the appearance of which has been shaped both by uplift during the Alpine Orogeny (when Africa collided with Europe towards the end of the Cretaceous period and the Alps were created) and differential rates of erosion. Once again the variable sequence of sedimentary beds combined with an exposed location cause regular rock falls, evidence of which is seen at the cliff's base.

At low tide, geometrically incised platforms reach approximately 250m into the sea and trace the cliffs' former extent. These wave-cut grooves are superficially similar to the patterning seen in limestone pavements. However, they are the result of different weathering processes. The potential confusion is not helped by the fact that these coastal features are commonly referred to as 'scars', just like the pavements themselves, although the latter are mainly located in uplands and montane environments.

JURASSIC
201–145 Ma

75 Kilve, Somerset

Kilve lies south-east of Nash Point, on the Bristol Channel's southern shore, and the cliffs are composed of similar Liassic limestone and shale. Consequently the coastal geomorphology mirrors the land it faces across the water, although the platforms extending from the cliffs on this side are nearly twice as wide. These ledges sweep outwards from the cliff in tiers, like a broad cascade of steps on their way down to the sea. As well as being visually striking, Kilve's rocks are famed for their abundant fossils, especially ammonites. However, this is not the only evidence of ancient life, as the shale beds are also rich in oil. Extensive natural gas and oil reserves found right the way across Britain and Ireland, and in the waters that surround them, are the decomposed remains of algae and bacteria that became trapped under muddy sea-floor sediments.

In 1924 Dr Forbes-Leslie founded The Shaline Company in order to extract the oil and a retort tower was built, which still stands a short distance from the beach. However, the process could not be made profitable and funding ran out. It is arguably a good thing that this method of producing oil was abandoned, as it would have had a drastic effect on what is today a designated Site of Special Scientific Interest (SSSI). The current technology for extracting oil and gas from shale is still somewhat controversial. The hydraulic extraction method, popularly referred to as 'fracking', is not without complications. Two earth tremors that occurred in Lancashire in 2011 have been linked to the practice and, elsewhere, it has been implicated in the contamination of underground aquifers used for drinking water.

76 Elgol, Strathaird Peninsula, Isle of Skye

Elgol is the scene of dramatic geological contrast, which accounts for it being one of the most celebrated (and most photographed) locations on the Isle of Skye. On this side of Loch Scavaig the rocks are Jurassic grey limestones, shales and pale golden sandstones dating from approximately 170 Ma, and it is the latter which forms this section of the foreshore and all the cliffs; while over on the loch's western margin the imposing Black Cuillin mountains were created during the Palaeogene period around 60 Ma and are of igneous origin (these will be returned to later, pages 170–1).

The cliffs, seen on the right, are of particular interest as they have been weathered into an unusual honeycomb-like texture (see detail on page 14). When this type of erosion is seen in a coastal environment it is caused by waves splashing onto rocks, leaving corrosive salt crystals to attack the cliffs. This process also affects rocks out of the direct reach of the sea, as salt spray can be carried some distance on the wind – which can be problematic for sandstone and limestone buildings in coastal settings. Curiously enough, this striking phenomenon is imitated in Renaissance and Victorian Classical architecture, where typically large stones are decorated with such patterns, often on a building's lower storey or around windows and doors. This process, termed rustication, is where various natural attributes are recreated in order to generate contrast with the smooth-dressed ashlar stones used as the primary construction material. In some cases the rustication is meant to resemble rough-hewn blocks straight from the quarry: the 'cyclopean' form. In other instances they are 'vermiculated' in imitation of worm burrows, although this category includes effects more closely resembling the texture of certain corals and of honeycomb erosion.

JURASSIC
201–145 Ma

77 Durdle Door, West Lulworth, Dorset

Nowhere is more emblematic of the Jurassic Coast than Durdle Door, where a narrow rib of Portland Limestone resting on Purbeck Limestone features one of the most recognisable arches in the British Isles. Durdle comes from the Middle English *thirl*, meaning hole or opening, which shares a common origin with Old English *thyrel* or *thurh*, meaning through. Combined with 'door' this is another example of a tautological place name, where the original meaning has been obscured.

Both types of limestone were formed when the upper reaches of a sandbank lay in shallows, and the calcium carbonate within the seawater coalesced around nuclei, either sand grains or minute shell fragments, to create tiny egg-like concretions known as ooids. These individual ooids were then cemented together with more calcium carbonate to produce oolitic limestone. This is highly valued as a monumental building material, and quarried on the nearby Isle of Portland and in the Cotswolds Hills further to the north.

Durdle Door is an example of a concordant coastline where rock beds have been folded upwards into a ridge aligned in parallel to the coast, thus forming a natural barrier against the tide. Although at one time this offered some protection to the softer Cretaceous chalks lying behind it, the limestone ridge was breached long ago, allowing the sea to eat into the cliffs and create circular coves on either side of the promontory. From above it resembles an upside down T-shape reaching into the sea, the horizontal component of which continues as a series of stacks. Another less advanced example of this process can be seen at Stair Hole approximately 1km to the east, where the ridge is still partially intact.

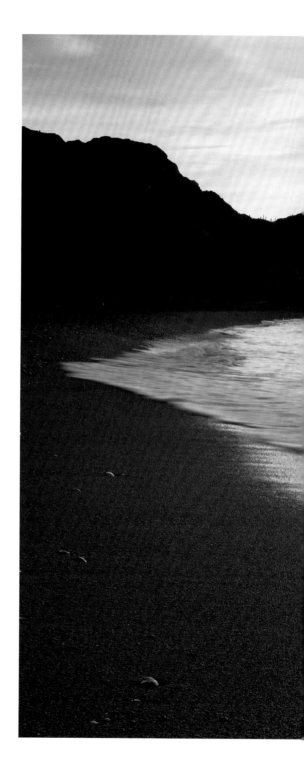

78 Black Nab, Saltwick Bay, North Yorkshire

A squat sea stack is often called a stump and the diminutive Black Nab is almost as wide as it is tall. It consists of an alternating sequence of marine sediments, and close inspection sheds light on the processes that create a sea stack as the division between the resistant sandstone and the weaker shale is clearly distinguishable. The shale is readily identifiable owing to its brittle-looking laminated (finely layered) structure. It is easy to imagine waves tearing away at the ragged edges and breaking the rock into thin flakes, whereas the sandstone is more robust and weathers to a smoother finish.

The cliffs along much of England's eastern shore are formed out of relatively soft sediments, meaning that, along with saltmarshes and dunes, they are the fastest changing section of Britain's coast. Much of the rock within Saltwick Bay's rapidly receding cliffs is mudstone, which offers even less resistance than shale to the full force of the North Sea. The retreat of the cliffs is already causing problems at Whitby just to the north, where the famous abbey is threatened by repeated rock falls slowly eating away at the ground near to its foundations; and at nearby Scarborough, where a massive landslide in 1993 completely destroyed a hotel. It is predicted that any sea-level rises will have major repercussions for this coastline and the communities living here. As with areas subject to flooding, it is becoming increasing difficult to get home insurance in locations prone to coastal erosion.

JURASSIC
201–145 Ma

79 Roseberry Topping, Newton under Roseberry, North Yorkshire

Further instances of Jurassic rocks are found inland from the coast, outcropping here in the Cleveland Hills and on the North Yorkshire Moors. The notable landmark Roseberry Topping consists of a sandstone cap protecting the shale below. The hill was once a perfect conical shape – and from some angles it still appears to be – but from this direction the effects of two landslips are easy to see. A major one occurred in 1922, when a large part of the south-western face subsided, followed by a lesser one in 1932. At the time, these incidents were blamed on the mining operations less than 1km south-east of the summit, which have since fallen into disuse. Geologists now know that the hillside is riddled with faults and gaps, meaning that the subsidence could have occurred with or without the mine's presence.

Roseberry Topping appears to have had symbolic significance for the ancient settlers of this landscape, which may have been due to its former sugarloaf-shaped profile. This makes it distinct from the rest of the Cleveland Hills, and is the probable reason for the burial of a Bronze Age hoard of axes and sickles on its slopes, which was uncovered in 1826. Later it became associated with the Vikings who invaded Britain at the end of the eighth century, and this is the source of the peak's name. Known as Óðins Bjarg, or Odin's Crag, after the Nordic God, it then mutated to Othensberg ('berg' meaning mountain) and some other variations, including Ouseberry, before making the transition to Roseberry. As 'berry' is derivative of 'berg' the addition of 'Topping' is superfluous as it derives from 'Toppen', another Old Norse word meaning hill.

80 Golden Cap, Seatown, Dorset

At 191m above sea level, Golden Cap is the highest point along England's south coast, and is one of the key locations along the Jurassic Coast World Heritage Site. The hill is mainly composed of Jurassic mudstone that is subject to occasional landslides, which creates the characteristic slumped shape and two distinct ledges known as Shorne Cliff and Wear Cliffs. As these slips extend towards the sea, the leading edge is washed away thus removing the supporting base that prevents further material from collapsing.

The uppermost section of the hill is formed from a golden sandstone known as the Upper Greensand that dates from the succeeding Cretaceous period. At first Upper Greensand seems a misleading term; however it refers to the appearance of newly exposed surfaces that are a rich green because of the mineral glauconite. Once they are subjected to the elements the glauconite oxidises to a gold colour hence the Golden Cap name, although this is less obvious than it once was because the cliff-top vegetation is now much denser.

The transition between the Jurassic and Cretaceous strata marks an unconformity. Owing to the break-up of Pangaea, Britain and Ireland underwent tectonic uplift during the Jurassic, which meant that the rocks forming this coastline were tilted eastwards and the intervening sequences of beds were eroded away before the greensand was deposited. This upheaval and parting of continents went on initially to create the northern portion of the Atlantic Ocean, followed by the southern section during the Cretaceous. This in turn began the closing of the Tethys Ocean, a process that was completed around 15 Ma.

81 Thornwick Nab, Flamborough Head, East Yorkshire

Thornwick Nab is an odd-shaped chalk formation jutting out from Flamborough Head, which is England's northernmost limit of this rock type, although there are a few localised deposits in western Scotland. Chalk is made from the remains of algae called coccolithophores that are so minute that they can be seen only with the help of an electron microscope. It is classed as limestone although the percentage of calcium carbonate it contains is much higher than in other types, making it bright white and easily recognisable. As the rock is the dominant feature, the period is named after it – *creta* being the Latin for chalk.

After a major drop in sea level at the end of the Jurassic the water began to rise again during the Cretaceous. Initially the sea did not cover the whole of Britain and Ireland, and it was not until later on in the period that rising waters flooded all of the British Isles. With this came the widespread deposition of chalk and as there was little exposed land from which sediments could be eroded, the rock is exceptionally pure. Most of the chalk has since weathered away, leaving the primary concentrations in east and south England and in Northern Ireland.

Thornwick Nab's tiered arrangement demonstrates differential rates of erosion, the more resistant beds forming a platform that is visible only at low tide. This is riddled with gaps and dotted with flint nodules, which is a kind of glassy and exceptionally tough sedimentary rock coalesced from the silica derived from sea sponge skeletons dissolved in seawater (see detail on page 14). Contributing to the formation's odd appearance is a layer of rich-brown boulder clay. This sediment is even more vulnerable to weathering than the chalk, becoming sticky and slippery when wet. The remains of the clay on top of the nab are shaped into pointed 'hats', making it unlike anything else in the British Isles. An archway intersects Thornwick Nab's two 'towers', but because erosion above and below are converging it is only a matter of time before this link crumbles. In 1984 an even more dramatic collapse befell a larger arch 500m to the south-east at North Landing, and the remaining stack disintegrated within months.

82 Devil's Dyke, Fulking, West Sussex

The chalk of south-east Britain is part of a group of sedimentary beds folded upwards during the Alpine Orogeny into a large structure known as the Weald–Artois anticline, which runs between The Weald in Kent and the Artois region of north-eastern France. As with all anticlines, the oldest rocks form the core and are revealed as later deposits are stripped away. The chalk is the youngest component and is found on the outer edge where it persists as a range of rolling hills and elevated plains intersected by river valleys, most notably the North and South Downs.

The Devil's Dyke is the largest dry valley, or combe, in Britain and one of the main geomorphological attractions of the South Downs. In the absence of evidence for the processes that carved it, the Devil was again invoked as the culprit. In the apocryphal account the Devil was digging a trench through the hillside in order to let in the sea, a mere 6km away, and flood the churches of the Weald, only he was disturbed and the task was never completed. However, anyone versed in reading the landscape can see that the dyke's classic V-shape indicates that it was formed by a river, not by the Devil or by glaciation for that matter, as the latter process creates u-shaped valleys. Indeed the glaciation that occurred after these rocks were laid down never reached this far south. Even so, the chalk was bound by permafrost and became saturated with seasonal meltwaters from snowfields. This led to soil fluction that carried sediments down the deepening valley and, when the periglacial conditions ended, meltwaters flooded along the channel, removing loose material and carrying it out to sea.

83 White Cliffs of Dover, St Margaret's Bay, Kent

The White Cliffs are the exposed edge of the North Downs and they face Continental Europe across the Straits of Dover, which is the narrowest part of the English Channel. Arriving from France by boat, the bright chalk is the first impression travellers have of Britain and this has secured the cliffs' iconic status. The chalk retains its brilliancy owing to weathering of the surface, which is so soft it is liable to leave traces on hands and clothes. The shining whiteness is illusory, as from close quarters the chalk has a greenish pallor caused by an algal film, which is an apt outcome for rock that is itself formed from algae. The organisms that populate the cliff are in themselves destructive, weakening the rock as they consume mineral nutrients and leaving it more vulnerable to the onslaught of waves. This is known as bioerosion and occurs wherever there are rocks to inhabit. Algae and lichens may look innocuous, but they are slowly breaking down even the hardest of surfaces.

The fact that Britain 'begins' here is a quirk of geological fate and climatic variations. During the Neogene, land was uplifted off the Straits of Dover and this country was attached to Continental Europe via a low-lying chalk plain. Although there were seaways linking the Atlantic Ocean to its offshoot, the North Sea, throughout the period, these passages moved around, sometimes following the English Channel's current course and at other times crossing northern France. Then, between 16,000 and 12,000 years ago, sea levels rose by 120m and Britain was made into an island. The English Channel has only really existed since the end of the most recent glaciation, around 8,000 years ago, with the sea reaching familiar levels around 6,700 years ago. All this is evidence, if any were needed, that geological manoeuvres pay no attention to political and sovereign boundaries.

84 Hunstanton Cliff, Hunstanton, Norfolk

Norfolk is so often dismissed as a rather flat county, and while that is partly true it is also home to some of England's most striking cliffs. At Hunstanton, a base of Carstone – a chocolate-coloured sandstone conglomerate – is overlain by Red Chalk and topped by white Lower Chalk beds. Although white chalk is not unusual for this part of the country, the red rock, which changes from a deep shade at the bottom to pink at the top, is altogether more remarkable and the contrast between the two is stunning. The vivid colouration is caused by the presence of Limonite, an iron-rich ore that has been oxidised on exposure to the air. Limonite is used as an ochre pigment in paints and is in the group known as the earths, producing a range of browns including the burnt sienna of the red chalk through to deep and muted raw umber.

Humans have a long held a fascination for these earths and they have inspired the imagination for many thousands of years. The practice of applying colourful clays to the body, often in patterns of spiritual and social significance, is still conducted by many tribal peoples. Celtic myths tell of the Fer Dearg or 'Red Men', who are thought to have derived their body paint from the bog iron common throughout the Irish Midlands. Elsewhere, these precious pigments were carved into trinkets, some of which have been dated to 75,000 years old, or daubed over rockfaces in sheltered locations or deep inside caves illuminated by little more than a smoking torch. Today's artists still value metallic oxides as they produce colours with natural richness and depth. It has taken many years research to successfully emulate them with synthetic alternatives.

85 The White Rocks, Portrush, County Antrim ⟹

This section of the Antrim coast is the most exposed area of chalk in Northern Ireland, and the rocks are regularly attacked by raging North Atlantic storms. It may then seem surprising that these chalk cliffs resist weathering better than their counterparts in the south and east of England, with which they share a common origin. During the Palaeogene, a few million years after the chalk was laid down volcanic activity took place in Northern Ireland. Basalt flowed over the chalk, baking and recrystalising it through contact metamorphism into a harder form known as Ulster White Limestone. Limestone that has undergone high-grade metamorphism is classed as marble, but having experienced only contact metamorphism these rocks are not altered to such a degree. Despite this relative hardness, the chalk is not immune to wave erosion, and where there is deep jointing between beds the sea carves labyrinthine structures. One of the best places to see these formations is White Rocks on Curran Strand, which includes masterpieces such as the Wishing Arch, seen here framing another headland that also incorporates an archway.

Northern Ireland's extensive chalk deposits are now only visible at the surface as two narrow bands confined to the edges of the Antrim Plateau basalt flow, although they do continue beneath it. This eruption was one of many events within a global upsurge in volcanic activity at the boundary between the Cretaceous and the Palaeogene, which ultimately gave rise to the largest volcanic feature on earth: the Deccan Traps in India. The increased volcanics threw large amounts of dust into the atmosphere, a problem exacerbated by the asteroid impact that created the vast Chicxulub crater off the Yucatán Peninsula in Mexico. Together, these catastrophic episodes initiated a downward spiral where dust clouds blocked sunlight and prevented photosynthesis, causing plants to die off and the food chain to collapse. This was the trigger for the Cretaceous–Palaeogene extinction event, when many species perished, most spectacularly nearly all of the non-avian dinosaurs, and marked the end of the Mesozoic Era and beginning of the Cenozoic Era (Greek: 'new life').

PALAEOGENE 66–23 Ma
NEOGENE 23–2.6 Ma

86 Carrick-a-Rede, Ballycastle, County Antrim

The time interval included within the Palaeogene and the subsequent Neogene periods was once known as the Tertiary and, although this is strictly speaking a historical term, it is still evident in some literature. As the Palaeogene began, the relative calm of the Cretaceous period was abruptly shattered at Carrick-a-Rede as an explosive volcano ripped through the recently deposited chalk and mudstone beds, throwing them into the air along with volcanic 'bomb' fragments from within the volcano. As the ash cloud settled it coalesced into a hard agglomerate from which the bombs clearly protrude. The 20m gap that was once the volcano's vent is now spanned by a rope bridge 30m above the waves. This was constructed by fishermen, who used it as the main method of accessing the island where, for over 250 years, they positioned nets to take advantage of the fact that Carrick-a-Rede (or 'Rock in the Road') is on the westward migration route of the Atlantic salmon. Originally there was just a single hand-rope to help with balancing when crossing, but the modern rope bridge is a much safer design and provides a rare opportunity to stand suspended above the vent of a volcano, albeit an extinct one.

The Palaeogene was the last period in which any new volcanic rocks were created across Britain and Ireland. Eruptions and lava flows occurred along a line running from Ireland via west Wales to the Hebrides. The volcanism was caused as Laurasia, the largest surviving fragment of Pangaea, was rifted apart and the North Atlantic continued to open up along the course of where the Iapetus Ocean had existed previously (Iapetus being the father of Atlas in Greek mythology). As the Earth's crust stretched, hot spots breached the surface in this zone. However, all igneous activity ceased by 50 Ma, at which point sedimentary deposition once again became the primary means of rock formation. This latter phase continued into the Neogene and produced much less obvious landforms when compared with the dramatic features for which the British Tertiary Volcanic Province (the term for all of Britain and Ireland's Palaeogene eruptions) is renowned.

87 Giant's Causeway, County Antrim

The Antrim Plateau is the largest area of volcanic rock within Northern Ireland and the lava is 1,800m thick. The basalt spreads across most of Antrim, smothering the underlying chalk and reaching into neighbouring counties. It is likely it that it once extended far beyond what can be seen today. Where the Antrim Plateau meets the sea it forms cliffs that are in themselves impressive enough, but are overshadowed by the Giant's Causeway's 40,000 mostly hexagonal columns, which are among the planet's finest examples of columnar faulting. The causeway and the 6km of coast extending between Causeway Head and Benbane Head are listed as an UNESCO World Heritage site, as the geomorphology is key to our understanding of the earth's geological evolution.

It makes sense that such an awe-inspiring location should have its own foundation myth, so yet again the landscape's shape is attributed to the hands of a giant. It is said that the larger-than-life warrior Fionn mac Cumhaill, or Finn McCool, built the causeway across the sea to Scotland in order to fight his Scottish counterpart Benandonner. This part of the tale is agreed upon but from then on the story diverges. In one version Fionn fell asleep on the way to meet his foe and Benandonner sought him out, and in another variation a passing boatman told Fionn that Benandonner was the larger giant. Whichever way the story started, it ended in Fionn's hurried return to his wife Oonagh. Quick-witted Oonagh suggested that he be disguised as their baby so when Benandonner arrived to see such a enormous infant, he assumed that his father must be of truly gargantuan proportions and fled, destroying the causeway as he went.

This story had enduring appeal and it was not until 1768 that a natural origin was confirmed when pioneer volcanologist Nicholas Desmarest wrote captions to accompany engravings of the causeway included in the French *Encyclopédie* (based upon Susanna Drury's widely seen paintings), suggesting a volcanic process. Even then his observations were disputed by other geologists, known as the Neptunists who claimed that basalt was formed as a precipitate of seawater.

PALAEOGENE 66–23 Ma
NEOGENE 23–2.6 Ma

88 Fingal's Cave, Staffa, Inner Hebrides

The narrative of Fionn mac Cumhaill and Benandonner also takes inspiration from Staffa, an island near Mull off Scotland's west coast. Staffa lies approximately 140km north-north-east of Causeway Head, and it is easy to visualise a continuation of the Giant's Causeway leading all the way to it, which lends some credence to the legend. Although the seabed consists of the same lava, there has never been a direct connection between the two locations. However, it does demonstrate that previous generations recognised the similarities and judged the sites to be of common origin, even if they had no scientific context in which to frame it. These remarkable landforms make it plain that regardless of the divided history of Britain and Ireland's landscape, these islands were born of the same geological processes and, but for a relatively recent rise in sea level, would lie closer together. During the most recent glaciation, Staffa was part of a larger island including Mull, Iona and the Treshnish Isles, and was sited much nearer the Scottish coastline. However, as the ice melted and sea levels rose, Staffa was overwhelmed and reduced to a diminutive 1km by 500m.

Staffa is shaped from three separate lava pulses, although its main attraction is the perpendicular basalt columns created from the second flow. The island is named after this characteristic, as visiting Vikings were reminded of their houses built from vertically arranged tree-trunks and *staffa* is the Old Norse for 'stave' or 'pillar'. The island's most well known feature is 20m high and 75m long Fingal's Cave, renamed in the eighteenth century after Fionn mac Cumhaill by Scot's poet James Macpherson. In the original Gaelic it was called An Uamh Bhin, or 'the melodious cave', a reference to the musicality of crashing waves resonating within the chamber. This is certainly no ordinary setting and, after visiting the island in the 1830s, Felix Mendelssohn was inspired to compose the celebrated Hebrides Overture.

PALAEOGENE 66–23 Ma
NEOGENE 23–2.6 Ma

89 Binevenagh, Limavady, County Derry/Londonderry

Binevenagh, or Binn Foibhne, is named after Foibhne, the son of the Celtic chief Taircheltar, who is alleged to have been killed on the hilltop. The escarpment reaches 385m above sea level and is at the western limit of the Antrim Plateau overlooking the Magilligan peninsula's lowlands. The basalt cap has protected the Cretaceous, Jurassic and Triassic rocks lying beneath, which are revealed at the escarpment's eroded foot. The hill has been affected by sizeable rotational landslides that occur when sections of cliff slip forwards from a weakened base, almost as if the land had been scooped out from underneath. The phenomenon is easy to identify as when a rotated block comes to rest it is slightly tilted back towards the plateau. These attributes give Binevenagh the appearance of battlements, and a local folktale recalls how a Viking raiding party, intent on sacking Derry monastery, turned on their heels when they sighted the crags through a shroud of mist, as they mistook them for a castle of prodigious dimensions.

The soil created from the erosion of the mafic rock is particularly fertile, with just the right structure and balance of elements needed to make the hilltop an ideal habitat for a diverse range of upland bog flora. Historically Binevenagh was valued as a natural apothecary and Irish herbalists helped spread its fame as a source of rare plant ingredients, the like of which could not be found elsewhere. This rich flora was also credited for bestowing a delicious flavour on the Magilligan honey which, as a result, commanded higher prices than any other. Today the plants are protected from the attentions of those who would pick them as is the area is a designated nature reserve.

PALAEOGENE 66–23 Ma
NEOGENE 23–2.6 Ma

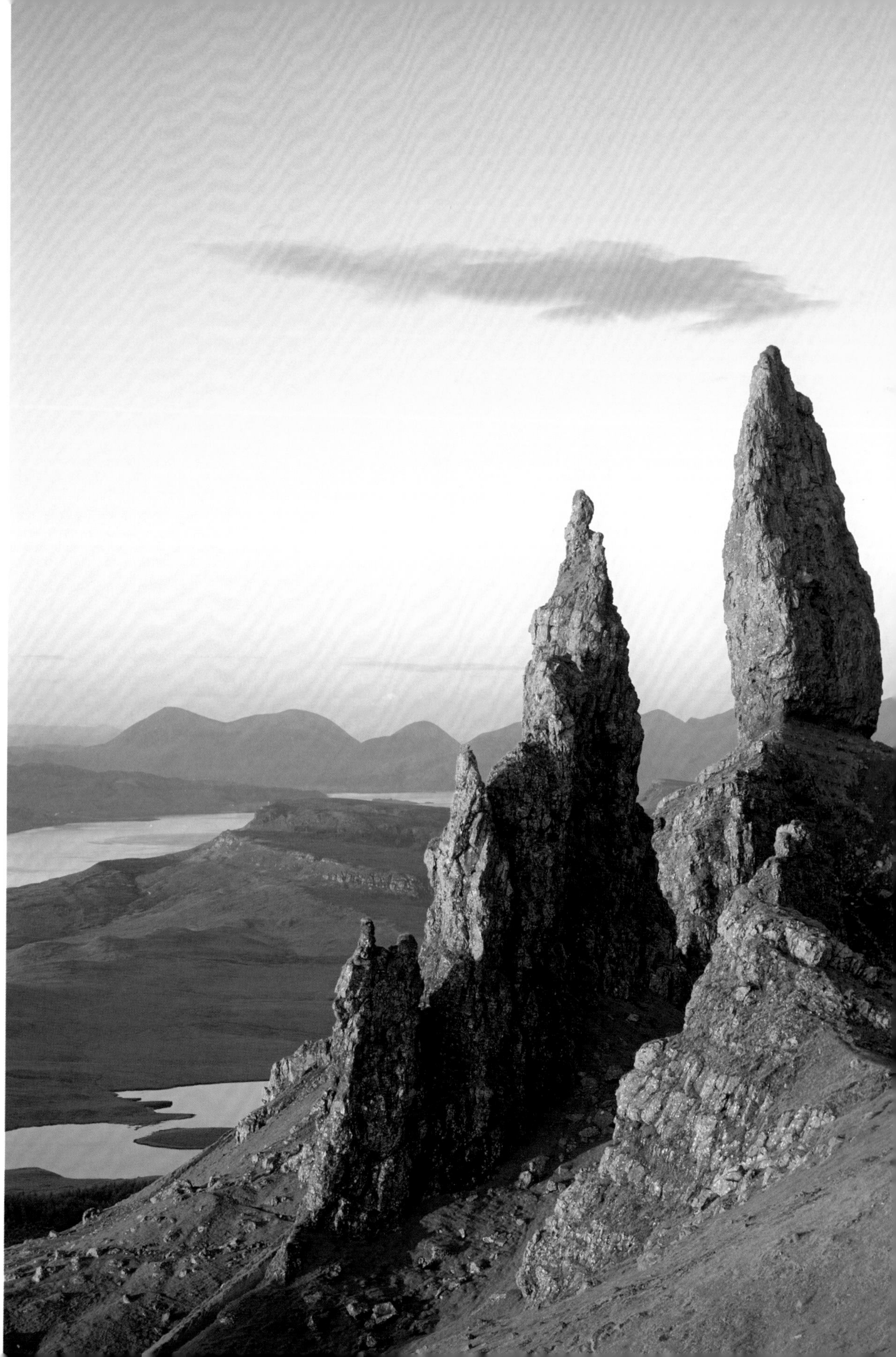

90 The Old Man of Storr, Trotternish peninsula, Isle of Skye

The Trotternish peninsula's landscape echoes the Antrim Plateau with which it shares many structural similarities, although it is 200m higher. Here on Skye the basalt that issued from fissures in Earth's crust spread out over the top of Jurassic shales. This unstable combination initiated the largest landslide in Britain, measuring an impressive 2km wide, and is responsible for such unusual landforms as these pinnacles, the biggest of which is the Old Man of Storr. Where the basalt has come to rest it sits directly on top of softer shales banked up with soil, which are undercut to a precarious degree and this is especially pronounced when standing directly beneath the Old Man. This grouping is a short distance downhill from the main cliff, The Storr, where they stand guard over an area known as The Sanctuary. The mountain, situated just over 2km from the coast and reaching 719m above the sea, is aptly named, coming as it does from the Old Norse *stórr* meaning 'great' or 'huge'.

Beyond the Old Man, and Loch Leathen at its foot, more basalt escarpments are seen leading all the way down to the sea. These rocks have been inclined by about 40° from the horizontal, an uplift occurring fairly soon after the lava had solidified. The jointed layers, the appearance of which is enhanced by weathering, represent the separate pulses of magma erupted over the course of many thousands of years. Together they form the plateau lava series that outcrops across most of northern and western Skye. The basalt extends to the south-west where it underlies the Black and Red Cuillin mountains, both of which ranges are seen on the horizon and, before erosion, it was around 1,200m thick.

91 The Quiraing, Trotternish peninsula, Isle of Skye ⇒

A few kilometres north of The Storr, the escarpment continues and manifests itself as the Quiraing, a convoluted and acoustically strange kingdom of basalt. Hidden among towering rock spires, some of which bear intimidating names such as The Prison and The Needle, is the miniature plateau called The Table, seen here from the uppermost of two tiers. These horizontal areas are an associated feature of 'trap' landscapes, which are characterised by successive basalt floods forming stepped ridges. As the lava cooled and gas bubbles worked their way upwards, the solidifying rock ended up with a more aerated texture towards the top. This vesicular portion was then more easily eroded and, once this material was stripped away, flat-topped steps of harder basalt remained. The scenery has been complicated still further by the extensive landslide that affected the whole escarpment although, unlike other cliffs along the Trotternish peninsula, the area around the Quiraing is still on the move and the road that runs beneath it has to be repaired annually.

Quiraing is another name with Viking heritage and originates from 'kvi' and 'rand', translating as 'round fold' via the Gaelic *Cuith-raing*. The reference to a fold, being a livestock enclosure, certainly accords with the story that the island's shepherds used The Table as a place to keep their flocks of sheep safe from marauding Vikings. If so, it was an inspired choice, as to find it one needs to know it is there. Even with a detailed map in hand it is not easy, and accessing it requires scrambling up a narrow footpath over a scree-covered slope winding between precipitously steep rocks that loom threateningly like the protective spines of a colossal petrified reptile.

92 Black Cuillin from Glenbrittle, Isle of Skye

Once seen, the Black Cuillin are not easily forgotten, as most of the range's peaks are well over 900m, although some nearly reach 1,000m, and they cover an area of more than 10km². The plateau lava series that makes up northern Skye extends underneath the huge volcanic centre that created both the Black and nearby Red Cullin. The Black Cuillin are the exposed magma chambers that existed at the roots of what were once massive volcanoes. As the molten basalt within them cooled slowly at depth, it created coarse-grained mafic rocks, including gabbro, which are frequently intruded by dolerite dykes. The adjacent Red Cullin, or Red Hills, are instead composed of granite create during a later phase of this igneous activity.

These rocks have a peculiarity that can seriously hamper navigation, which must be done with map and compass as clouds so often obstruct the view. Iron-rich magnetite deposits within the gabbro are capable of deflecting a compass needle from magnetic north, making readings

misleading at best. However, the gabbro does have one redeeming quality, as its rough texture makes it a reliable surface to scramble across. This is offset, however, by the dolerite that weathers to a glassy-smooth finish and is especially treacherous when wet. These combined difficulties only serve to reinforce the Cuillin's formidable reputation, and the range is considered by many to be the ultimate British mountaineering experience.

The mythological interpretation of how the Cuillin came to be is not so far from the truth. The story relates how the personification of Winter Cailleach Bheur, also known as the Old Hag, held Spring's beloved hostage and in desperation he asked for the Sun's help in returning her to him. To thwart Cailleach Bheur, the Sun threw down a fiery spear that split the earth open, and from this crack molten rock poured out to create the mountains, at which point Spring was able to rescue his love. Remove the fiery spear from the description and it closely recalls basalt issuing from a crustal rift.

93 Rùm Cuillin from Cleadale, Eigg, Small Isles

Eigg's central upland area is wrought from basalt lavas that created high escarpments. This contrasts with the island's west coast, where beautiful beaches, fringed with pale Jurassic sandstone, feature silver-grey sands that are a mixture of white quartz from sandstone and black basalt grains. This particular stretch is known as the 'Singing Sands' because of its amusing habit of squeaking when walked across. Rùm, the largest of the Small Isles, lies 6km across the sea. In spite of being more than twice the size of Eigg the population is considerably lower due as most of the island is taken over by the Rùm Cuillin. These peaks strongly resemble their more famous namesakes on Skye and, like the Black Cuillin, are formed from intrusive gabbros. However, the basaltic lava on Rùm had a much higher silica content so that where it reached the surface it was released with explosive force, resulting in pyroclastic flows. The remains of this event are seen in rocks called rhyodacites found around the volcano's margins.

The saying goes that mountains make their own weather and these mountainous islands are like cloud factories. When moist air rises abruptly from sea level it cools rapidly and clouds of condensed vapour quickly form. This image illustrates what happens when a fair-weather cumulus cloud draws on the potential of the damp air above the mountains and becomes something rather more sinister. The weather associated with mountains helps explain some of their aura. It is not just that they are huge – as this is obvious – it is that are they substantial enough to influence the weather.

Geology and weather are closely linked systems and are two aspects of a complex global dynamic. The movements of continents, the expansion and contraction of oceans, and the raising and weathering of mountains all impact on the circulation of air and oceanic currents. Combined with the recurring catastrophes of large-scale volcanic activity, gas escaping from cracks in the seabed and massive meteor impacts it is surprising that the Earth has remained habitable. No matter what the atmospheric conditions are, life has proved to be remarkably adaptable.

94 Caisteal Abhail, Glen Sannox, Arran

Arran's northern half is dominated by a granite batholith formed by hotspot activity associated with the North Atlantic Ocean's growth. Subsequent erosion created a dramatic area of mountains and corries, including the sharply serrated Caisteal Abhail, which is the second highest peak on the island. Erratics, transported from this granite interior, are found across Arran and include those found resting on the New Red Sandstone shore at Merkland Point. The mountain's distinguishing feature is a deep gash in the ridge to the east of the summit known as Ceum na Caillich or 'The Witch's Step', which once again invokes the Old Hag and is no doubt an allusion to the cruel nature of this notoriously difficult climb.

Caisteal Abhail translates from the Gaelic as 'Castle of the Ptarmigan' and Arran has the most southerly population of the birds. Ptarmigans live on high ground only and, although once found as far south as the Lake District, encroachment on their habitat by humans has forced their retreat north of the border. The mountain is one of a cluster of summits that, when viewed from the Ayrshire coast, is said to resemble the profile of a recumbent figure, which is why this area of mountains is often referred to as 'The Sleeping Warrior'. Admittedly it does require a sideways look and some imagination. However, when the setting sun reveals it in silhouette the likeness is quite convincing.

95 Slieve Binnian, near Annalong, County Down

The Mourne Mountains cover an area of 24 x 13km and are carved from granite batholiths towering above a coastal plain next to the Irish Sea. Although at 747m Slieve Binnian is only the third highest peak in the range (Slieve Donard, seen on the right, exceeds it by more than 100m), it has the more interesting summit landforms. The numerous tors, arranged along the crest and the subsidiary hills, explain the Gaelic name Sliabh Binneain that means 'Mountain of the Little Horns'. These protruding features make the peak easily identifiable from a distance.

The range is consists of two plutonic centres: one in the east that has the highest mountains and another in the west, both of which came into existence around 56 Ma during the middle stages of the igneous activity within the British Tertiary Volcanic Province. The granite rests on a bed of Silurian shales and slates, and the highest peaks formed as a result of cauldron subsidence occurring when a 10km round shale block sank into the Earth's crust. The displaced magma was forced up over the sides of the descending block filling the space it once occupied.

The land between the mountains and the sea is still referred to as the Kingdom of Mourne, after the Mughdoma clan that migrated here around 700 years ago. Long before this, from around AD 300, tradition states that the district was ruled from a stronghold on Slieve Binnian by a cow-herd king called Boirche, and he is remembered in the range's historical name: Beanna Boirche. This enchanting place directly inspired another celebrated kingdom, the fantastical realm of Narnia. The author C.S. Lewis grew up in nearby Belfast and speaking of the Mournes he said 'I have seen landscapes which, under a particular light, made me feel that at any moment a giant might raise his head over the next ridge.' These monumental mountains weave a captivating spell by means of their romantic otherworldliness and they evoke a time before humans had dominion over all, and the creatures of the imagination were pushed to the hinterland.

PALAEOGENE 66–23 Ma
NEOGENE 23–2.6 Ma

While igneous events continued elsewhere in Britain, the rocks of southern England were being laid down in a more sedate process. As the Palaeogene progressed marine conditions became more widespread, resulting in the creation of partially consolidated rocks across the London and Hampshire Basins, the latter of which are magnificently revealed in the Alum Bay cliffs. These sand and clay beds formed during the Eocene, the middle epoch of the Palaeogene, and their multicoloured appearance is a textbook example of iron-oxide chemistry, each of the twenty-one hues resulting from changes in the environmental conditions. The beds at the bay's northern limit (only just visible on the left) are the youngest and nearly horizontal. Those on the right are older and practically perpendicular due to monoclinal folding that took place during the Alpine Orogeny, the event that also created the Weald-Artois anticline and folded the Purbeck limestone on the Dorset coast.

These older beds abut a vertically oriented unconformity where they meet Cretaceous chalk, seen here in the foreground. The chalk forms the bay's southern rim and its other famous feature – The Needles sea stacks.

In the Victorian era the coloured sands became all the rage and, along with The Needles, they became a popular visitor attraction. The sands were used to fill decorative glass jars and to create pictures known as marmotinto. At that time visitors were allowed to dig for their own materials, whereas today such a thing is inconceivable not just because the cliffs are dangerously unstable, to which the frequent landslips attest, but for the sake of their future preservation. Now sand is collected only when slips occur and these happen often enough to provide plenty of material for the many tourists keen to continue the tradition of making their own souvenirs.

97 Hengistbury Head, Mudeford, Dorset

Hengistbury Head is a 36m cliff of alternating sand deposits laid down during the Palaeogene, of which only the upper beds are visible here, as dunes encroach significantly at the southernmost point. The strata is interspersed with regular rows of ironstone 'doggers', which are iron-rich sandstone nodules formed in a bog from decaying matter mixed with settling sediments. The doggers are exceptionally hard and are revealed when the softer sands erode and the cliff retreats. Throughout the 1850s many doggers were removed from the cliffs because of their valuable iron content but now, thankfully, the site is a Nature Reserve and the removal of rocks is prohibited.

The headland is capped with a layer of coarse river gravel dating from the Pleistocene, the first epoch of the succeeding Quaternary period. Mudeford Spit's mobile dunes are another Quaternary feature and the beach is growing as a result of the tide transporting sand from along the coast at Bournemouth, a short distance to the west, in a process called longshore drift. There, instead of accepting the erosion, the beach is replenished artificially with sand from other sources and reinforced with wooden groynes – a battle of wills that nature will ultimately win.

The last 2 million years have been marked by a fluctuating climate with seventeen cycles of cold temperatures (glaciations) interspersed by warm interludes (inter-glacials). During this period human populations began to migrate from Africa with some heading north when the land was free of ice. A 520,000-year-old *Homo heidelbergensis* leg bone found in Sussex in 1994 provided the earliest evidence of Britain's colonisation, predating the onset of the severe Anglian glaciation by 40,000 years. Subsequent finds of stone tools at sites in England and Wales have pushed this ancient occupation of Britain back to at least 700,000 years ago. As the ice ebbed and flowed, populations kept in step, with waves of immigration and emigration driven by the climate. When conditions were at their harshest they left Britain and Ireland entirely. Traces of human occupation found at Hengistbury Head date back to the European Palaeolithic, around 11,000 years ago, just as the most recent glaciation was ending. This marked the start of the Holocene epoch and began the interglacial period in which we are still living.

98 Clew Bay, Westport, County Mayo

When the Anglian glaciation was at its height (480,000–425,000 years ago) an ice sheet reached from the North Pole across Britain and Ireland except for a small part of southern Wales, and a portion of England lying to the south of Bristol and London, diverting the River Thames to its present course in the process. After a warm interglacial episode, two less severe glaciations followed: the Wolstonian and the Devensian, the latter of which peaked between 26,000–19,000 years ago – the Last Glacial Maximum (LGM) – and ended only 10,000 years ago.

Ice and meltwaters are largely responsible for the landforms we are familiar with today, as few rocks escaped the effects of glaciation. As rocks were ground down, broken fragments were distributed far and wide by ice sheets. Known collectively as glacial drift, these loosely consolidated boulder clays, gravels and silts are the least-noticed addition to the Quaternary landscape, but they represent the greatest contribution by area. This type of deposit is well illustrated by miniature hills called drumlins (from the Gaelic *druim*, meaning rounded hill or mound) that are a notable addition to the scenery of central and northern parts of Ireland. As transported sediments become snagged on uneven bedrock they pile up into elongated humps oriented in line with the passing of the ice. The direction can be determined as a 'blunt' end faces into the flow whereas a drawn out 'tail' is created as the ice drags over the top. Reading these features it is clear that Clew Bay's drumlins were created by ice moving from west to east.

Clew Bay is a classic example of 'basket of eggs' style topography and the drumlin 'eggs' have been made easier to see because the low-lying land became flooded. At the beginning of each glacial period, sea levels drop as water gets turned into ice but they rise again as it melts. The present coastline came into being after the Last Glacial Maximum. This has left a hundred or so drowned drumlins visible, although some say that there are 365 islands, one for every day of the year – why let the facts get in the way of a good anecdote?

99 Chesil Beach and the Isle of Portland, Dorset

The 30km-long Chesil Beach is another highlight of the Jurassic Coast and is a shingle bar that connects Portland with the mainland and a road now runs along its course. It has been pushed towards the land from open water by waves large enough to fling shingle ashore. These occur during violent weather and the resulting landform is described as a storm beach, which gets repeatedly topped-up by waves coming straight off the Atlantic Ocean. The beach provides some protection for the land behind it and at the north-west end the shingle has piled up against the cliffs, enclosing a stretch of sea and creating a long and narrow tidal lagoon known as The Fleet in the process. The bar is an impressive sight, especially when viewed from Portland's high ground, ensuring its place in the nation's affections. Famously it was used as a setting in Ian McEwan's 2007 novel *On Chesil Beach*.

It was initially created approximately 20,000 years ago when the Devensian glaciation was still at its height, although the outline has changed many times since. The shingle is constantly on the move as it is reworked by the tide and the pebbles are graded by size along the beach, with the largest ones appearing towards the north-west end. Chesil is from the Old English word for shingle, *ceosel* or *cisel*. Shingle denotes a size rather than a type of rock and this beach, in common with many along England's south coast (like that seen on pages 148–9), is composed mainly of chert. When chert is tumbled smooth it has an opaque glassy surface and is easily identifiable as it shows pale pinks and red-browns from iron pigmentation, among the less richly-coloured pebbles.

100 Sands of Forvie, Newburgh, Aberdeenshire

Sand dunes, along with peat groughs, are among the primary landforms of the Holocene epoch. Following the melting of the last Scottish glaciers approximately 10,000 years ago, vast quantities of sandy sediments were transported by rivers to the coast and deposited offshore. However, as sea levels rose owing to the melting of the Scandinavian and North American ice sheets (peaking approximately 4,000 years ago), these sediments were reworked and deposited back onshore to form dunes.

The Sands of Forvie extend for 24km along the coast north of Aberdeen and reach a respectable 20m tall. The shifting sands are constantly redefined by wind, waves and the tide that together are marching the dunes northwards and, as such, the sands are described as an active geomorphological complex. Forvie village once stood here only a few hundred metres from the current shoreline located near the schist outcrop at Rockend. However, the dunes have since smothered everything but the twelfth-century church built at the settlement's highest point. The village appears to have been abandoned in the fifteenth century, although a fisherman's family lived here in an isolated croft well into the twentieth century.

The sands nearest the shore are largely mobile and therefore barren like the Sahara. However, where marram grass gains a hold, its dense root mats help 'fix' the sand in place, allowing other plants to colonise the dunes. Areas furthest from the shore are covered in various heathland species that benefit from Forvie having one of the least disturbed dune systems in Britain. A dune's age can be gauged by the plants growing on it, with the oldest being populated by the invasive creeping willow. Left unchecked it creates dense scrub at the expense of other flora, and transforms heath into woodland. An entire cycle from desert to budding woodland is evident here, and millions of years hence it will all have been compacted into sandstone beds potentially interspersed with coal layers formed from buried peat.

Entering the Anthropocene?

If a photograph could outlive a geological period, future viewers would not recognise the landscape represented, as time will have dismantled existing forms and built up new ones. However, even drawings only a few hundred years old can illustrate substantial changes as the land is remodelled from one generation to the next, or sometimes catastrophically during the course of just a few hours or days. This is nature but we are accelerating the process.

As past climatic fluctuations are encapsulated within the Earth's rocks, the geological record foretells the planet's future. Having analysed this and other data sources, many geologists and climatologists agree that a new epoch should be designated – the Anthropocene – in recognition of the human impact on environment. Most of these negative effects are attributed to activities that have taken place since the Industrial Revolution, which began in Britain in the late eighteenth century and was powered by coal. Burning this material on such an unprecedented scale triggered a rapid rise in carbon dioxide (CO_2) and sulphur dioxide levels, the latter of which caused the acid rain that blighted natural habitats and left a permanent impression on the stonework of some historical buildings. 'Clean Air' acts have led to a decline in domestic usage across Europe, although there is continued reliance on coal-fuelled power stations. Acid rain has been less widespread as a result but some countries still suffer its damaging effects. Unfortunately coal has largely been substituted by other fossil fuels such as gas and oil that are equally adept at releasing CO_2.

Others trace the origin of significant environmental change much further back in time, and cite the advent of agriculture as the turning point. This was when humans began to exert total control over nature and started deforestation on a large scale, removing the very trees that are the simplest line of defence against rising CO_2 levels. Plants have evolved in response to specific environmental niches and removing them alters both ecosystems and the atmosphere. Reshaping habitats has sown the idea that we have dominion over nature, and initiated a process of detachment which has become more pronounced as we each have less involvement in the growing of food and caring for the environment. It is this dislocated sense of our place in the world that for too long has kept us away from the realisation that what is bad for the planet is even worse for us.

Perhaps our fortunate position within the relatively habitable temperate zone of northern Europe, with little in the way of catastrophic events posing an immediate threat to life, has allowed complacency to set in. Few can be completely unaware of the threat of melting polar ice and rising sea levels, the anthropogenically-driven climatic change that is most widely spoken of in popular media, although to many this is a vague scenario beyond the realm of personal responsibility. No doubt those living on the coast with no high land to retreat to anticipate these effects more keenly, as do those whose fresh water supplies will be ruined as salt waters encroach. As populations increase and more people are forced to inhabit flood plains and coastal fringes these problems will only become more acute, with mass-migration from equatorial regions to high ground in the Northern Hemisphere a possible consequence. There are unsettling echoes here of the archetypal 'Great Flood' narrative that is common to many cultures. These stories may well contain within them an inherited memory of actual local events that led to significant loss of life, as sea level has varied considerably during the human occupation of the Earth, sometimes changing quite abruptly.

As polar ice continues to melt and warmer seas expand in volume, several coastal locations featured in this book could well disappear under the waves within our lifetimes. This possibility is exacerbated by the fact that although Scotland has been gently rebounding since the weight of the Devensian ice lifted, southern and eastern England, Wales and southern Ireland are actually sinking at a rate of roughly 1mm per year. London, which is built on clay deposits that are still settling, is actually subsiding at twice that rate. As island nations with extensive coastlines this issue cannot be ignored indefinitely.

Ice is a key regulator of atmospheric temperature because it reflects a large proportion of the Sun's rays, which has a cooling effect ultimately leading to glaciation. Each planetary surface has a measurable reflectiveness, or an albedo, and although that of ice is high, dark-coloured oceans have a low albedo and absorb solar energy which has a warming influence that in turn causes ice to melt. This is a delicately balanced system and, despite the fact that oscillating climate has been a contributing factor in Earth's evolution, the current rate of change – 1,000 years worth of warming in a little over 100 years, is worrying.

Core samples of polar ice reveal that CO_2 levels track global temperatures closely and as concentrations increase the climate warms, the so-called greenhouse effect. Atmospheric CO_2 has risen by one third in the last 200 years, half of which has taken place within the last thirty. Methane is another greenhouse gas that is cause for concern as it is twenty times more potent than CO_2 in its warming capabilities and is released during many natural and manmade processes, including decomposition of organic matter by anaerobic bacteria, coal-mining, the burning of natural gas and livestock farming. It is also escaping from melting permafrost at high latitudes where its effects have been put on hold while bound up in frozen peat bogs for many thousands of years. Methane is capable of decreasing oxygen levels and, although this may sound ominous, without this mechanism rising oxygen concentrations would increase the likelihood of devastating forest fires, releasing tonnes of CO_2 in the process.

These examples make plain the tangled relationships that sustain Earth's unusually stable atmosphere. Meanwhile humankind is engaged in an experiment with the atmosphere's geochemisty that no one, not even with the best-informed climatic modelling data, can predict the outcome of with certainty. One consequence that is hard to ignore is substantial changes in weather patterns. As I write forest fires rage across an unusually dry southern Europe, and water restrictions affecting south and east England due to sparse spring rainfall have only recently been lifted. Despite this MET Office records show that the summer of 2012 was among the wettest since records began in 1910, a fact that I can attest to living in northern England where episodic flooding is fast becoming the norm.

As a landscape photographer I am a keen observer of the seasons and have witnessed many anomalies over recent years, from the near absence of 'April showers' to plants flowering at odd times. Most images for this book were made during 2011–2012 and weather-wise those were the most challenging years of my professional life. It has been suggested that increasing summer ice-melt in Greenland is responsible for these altered weather patterns as the Arctic Ocean's surface temperature affects the course of the North Atlantic jet stream, the high altitude wind which determines European weather. 2012 saw the lowest recorded levels of summer polar ice, being just half of what they would have been only twenty-five years ago. A possible outcome of this is more rainfall in northern Europe and a drier climate in the south.

The dry conditions are a taste of the potential desertification that can transform viable agricultural land into a dustbowl, whereas excessive rainfall impacts negatively on crop yields and, in addition to flooding, can go on to cause landslips in geologically unstable areas. Landslips and fast-eroding coastlines pose both practical and philosophical problems. Rocks are deemed to be solid and are supposed to be a secure basis on which to build homes. When this thin veneer of stability crumbles the edifice of order on which lives are based is discarded and a whole series of planetary-wide mechanisms to which we pay far too little regard to unfolds in front of us.

Even though humans have proven themselves capable of adapting, we can exist only within a narrow spectrum of conditions, neither too hot nor too cold. If marked climatic shifts occur over a short timespan, there would be less chance of successfully meeting the new pressures. Past environmental changes may have been one of the spurs behind the development of human intelligence, as competition induced by fewer available resources during glaciations meant that many of our forebears perished and only those who were fittest, or smartest, survived to pass on their genes. It remains to be seen how we react collectively to the potentially huge environmental consequences waiting round the corner. Will we bury our heads in the sand? Come up with a technological solution that will allow us to keep on extracting huge amounts of energy and resources from the planet? Or learn to live within our means?

It is striking that in the 3,500 million years of life inhabiting the planet the oceans have never totally evaporated or frozen over completely, despite the cataclysmic events that have regularly taken place. This is one of the pieces of evidence put forward to support the notion that Earth is in effect a giant self-regulating organism consisting of all life in partnership with the surface rocks, the oceans and the air. This idea, known as the Gaia hypothesis (proposed by Lovelock and Margulis), states that each organism and every non-organic process has a function with a complex system that maintains a habitable environment and, if some part of this mechanism should go awry, then other processes will kick in to rebalance it. When rocks are broken down to provide the basic elements of life (partly because of erosion by life itself) and the resultant organisms are returned to the earth as limestone, coal and other organic compounds, it is not so hard to appreciate the eloquence of this idea.

If the Gaia hypothesis proves to be correct, then Earth is capable of healing itself over time. The reason that this is possible is because less than a third of the globe is covered by land and as yet the oceans, where the most important life resides (the billions of microscopic entities that are central to climate regulation), have so far been left relatively unexploited. The question is how many species will be extinguished during the time it takes to recover planetary equilibrium, and will the human animal be among the casualties? It would be a tragedy if the most significant act humankind ever performs is the universal depletion of finite resources and the unintended decimation of many lifeforms – some not yet known to science – simply because we failed to grasp our ecological responsibilities. For the larger the human population becomes, meaning more animals and plants would be required to nourish us, the more implicated we become in the processes that make an environment sustainable.

Earth is 4600 million years old and our presence here has been so fleeting as barely to register on the geological timescale – measuring less than 0.1% of the total span – and yet our influence has, within that time, become all-pervasive. Our status as an intelligent species is undermined in fundamental ways such as adherence to global economic models relying on continued growth, which requires the increasing use of raw materials to make products to sell and to power services. Where exactly are these extra resources to materialise from? There is only one Earth and, as investment in space travel declines and the possibility of colonising other planets returns to the realm of science fiction, connecting with the reality beneath our feet is the only option. That we are here at all to contemplate this dilemma is a strangely beautiful accident, and eventually all human experience will be reduced to a few fossils and many pieces of stubbornly persistent plastic created from polymers that fragment easily but are slow to degrade. Is it conceivable that at some point hence another sentient species will look back upon this time and, finding a layer of natural sediments replete with tiny brightly-coloured synthetic particles, classify it as the Plastic Age in an unconscious imitation of our own Stone Ages?

Further Reading & Useful Websites

Flannery, Tim, *We Are the Weather Makers: The Story of Global Warming* (Text Publishing, 2006)

Fortey, Richard, *The Hidden Landscape: A Journey into the Geological Past* (Bodley Head, 2010).

Hutton, James, *Theory of the Earth* (Edinburgh, 1788).

Lovelock, James, *Gaia: A New Look at Life on Earth* (Oxford, revised edition 2000).

Lyell, Charles, *Principles of Geology* (John Murray, 1830).

Stewart, Iain, & Lynch, John, *Earth: The Power of the Planet* (BBC Books, 2007).

Toghill, Peter, *The Geology of Britain: An Introduction* (Swan Hill Press, 2000).

Vitaliano, Dorothy B., *Legends of the Earth: Their Geologic Origins* (Indiana University Press, 1977).

British Geological Survey: www.bgs.ac.uk
Geological Survey of Ireland: www.gsi.ie
The Geological Society: www.geolsoc.org.uk

Glossary

aeolian wind generated geological processes

alluvial unconsolidated soil or sediments eroded and deposited by lakes, rivers and melting glaciers

anthropogenic a process that can be attributed to human actions

anticline an upwards fold

arête a knife-edge mountain ridge formed through glaciation, associated with corries

asthenosphere the highly viscous lower part of the upper mantle that is directly below the lithosphere

barrier beach a long and linear beach usually extending outwards into the sea

batholith a massive pluton

beck a mountain stream (northern English)

ben also beinn*, beanna^ and binn mountain (Anglicised Scottish and the Scots* and Irish^ Gaelic forms)

burn a small stream (Scottish, or 'alt' in Gaelic)

bwlch a gap between peaks (Welsh, also 'bealach' in Gaelic)

carn same as cairn, a loose pile of stones (Welsh)

conglomerate sedimentary rock with sizeable chunks of other rocks contained within it

corrie a round valley cut into a mountainside by glacial erosion

cross-bedding an inclined sedimentary structure formed as layers are deposited rather than through tilting due to subsequent Earth movements. This occurs in conjunction with ripples in fluvial settings and dunes in aeolian processes

cwm same as corrie (Welsh)

dyke long narrow structures formed through intrusion of molten rock into exisiting gaps, which can be steeply inclined or nearly vertical

eon the largest unit of geological time

epoch the fourth largest unit of geological time

era the second largest unit of geological time

fault rock fractures showing evidence of relative movement between surfaces

fluvial sediments associated with rivers and melting glaciers i.e. glaciofluvial

fold layers of rock bent or curved as a result of deformation

foliation internal layering within a rock unit, forming a plain along which the rock will fracture more easily

freeze-thaw cycle the cyclic changes in atmospheric temperature occurring over the course of a day or over the space of years that can cause erosion of rocks where ice forms in joints

geomorphology the study of landforms and the processes that shape them

glaciation a period within an ice age where the temperature is cold and glaciers advance

glacio-karst a landscape that has been weathered both by glacial ice and by water

igneous rocks of molten origin, both intrusive magma (plutonic) and extrusive lava (volcanic)

ignimbrite the deposits of a pyroclastic flow formed from ash and pumice fragments

interglacial a period within an ice age where the temperature is warm and glaciers retreat

invertebrate an animal with an exterior skeleton

ion an atom that is either positively or negatively charged dependent on the number of electrons

larst topography shaped by water where soluble rocks have been dissolved over to time to form characteristic features such as caves and pavements, often in limestone

laminated where rocks exist in in obviously separate layers, which can sometimes be split along the bedding plane as with slate

lithification when loose sediments are consolidated into solid rock

lithosphere composed of three elements: continental crust, oceanic crust and the partially molten upper reaches of the mantle

llyn lake (Welsh)

loch*, also lough^ lake (Scots* and Irish^ Gaelic). Lochan often denotes a small loch

Ma abbreviation: millions of years ago, also written mya

mantle the highly viscous layer between the crust and the Earth's outer core. It is divided itno sections, the upper mantle that includes the lower part of the lithosphere (the mantle that is directly below the crust) and the asthenosphere; the lower mantle and the mantle-core boundary

mélange an extensive area of rock composed of variable large fragments (from the French for mixture)

Mesolithic Middle Stone Age, dates vary across the globe

metamorphic exisiting rocks transformed by extreme heat and/or pressure

metasediment metamorphosed sediments

Neolithic New Stone Age, dates varxy across the globe

nuée ardente same as pyroclastic flow (French for fiery cloud)

ophiolite a piece of oceanic crust that has become detached from the seafloor and emplaced on land

orogeny a mountain building episode occurring as a result of continental collision

Palaeolithic Old Stone Age, dates vary across the globe

period the third largest unit of geological time

petroglyph an image or pattern carved into rocks with tools

periglacial environments and processes associated with freezing, such as 'freeze-thaw' cycles, rather than being directly affected by glacial ice

plate boundary where two continental plates meet, can be convergent (coming together), divergent (moving apart) or conservative (sideways movement)

pluton	an underground magma body, *see* igneous
protolith	the original rock type before being metamorphosed into an new form
pyroclastic flow	a fast-moving cloud of superheated gas, ash and rock fragments erupted from volcanoes
sedimentary	rocks formed from particles compressed into layers or 'beds' by the weight of accumulating sediments above
sill	horizontal seams of molten rock intruded parallel to existing bedding
strata	layer of sedimentary rock or soil featuring consistent characteristics that distinguish it from other layers
subduction	occurring at a convergent plate boundary where one section of crust moves underneath another and descends into the mantle
syncline	a downward fold
taigh, also tràigh	beach (Scots Gaelic)
tarn	small mountain lake often in a corrie
terrane	a geologically distinct area of rocks, usually covering a region, that is easily distinguished from the adjacent land
tombolo	a barrier beach that ties an island to the mainland
turbidite	a sedimentary deposit created by a turbidity current from an underwater avalanche
tuff	the hard deposits of a pyroclastic flow formed from ash and other fragments
uplift	a process that lifts rocks from their original position, often inclining them at an angle and sometimes simultaneously folding them
vertebrate	an animal with an interior skeleton
vesicles	gas bubbles trapped within lava as it cools
viscosity	the thickness of a fluid, water has a low viscosity whereas treacle's is high

CONTINENTS

Avalonia	The Palaeozoic microcontinent that included what is today the southern parts of Britain and Ireland, and which came into existence as a volcanic arc on the margin of Gondwana.
Baltica	The late-Proterozoic/early-Palaeozoic continent that today includes Europe and Asia (Eurasia), which went onto collide with the smaller Avalonia in the late Ordovician.
Gondwana	The early Palaeozoic supercontinent that included most of the landmasses of today's southern hemisphere. It was the southernmost of the two supercontinents, the other being Laurasia, that emerged when Pangaea divided in two.

Laurentia	This continent is now the core of today's North America Craton and has its origins in various Archean microcontinents that merged into one landmass during the Proterozoic. Late on in the Silurian period Laurentia went on to merge with Avalonia-Baltica, creating the Old Red Sandstone Continent and initiating the Caledonian Orogeny.
Laurasia	The northernmost of the two supercontinents, the other being Gondwana, that emerged when Pangaea divided in two. The name combines Laurentia and Eurasia, reflecting the fact that it included most of the landmasses now found in the northern hemisphere.
Pangaea	This single supercontinent takes its name from the Greek for 'entire Earth' and existed during the late-Palaeozoic and early-Mesozoic eras. It began to rift in the Triassic period and presaged the configuration of continents that we are familiar with today.
Old Red Sandstone Continent	aka Euramerica or Laurussia. The supercontinent created by the merging of Avalonia-Baltica with Laurentia.

OCEANS AND SEAS

Atlantic Ocean	The northern area of this ocean began to open up in the late Jurassic as Pangaea rifted and was followed by the southern section opening up during the succeeding Cretaceous period.
Iapetus Ocean	This ocean of the southern hemisphere existed during the late-Proterozoic and early-Palaeozoic eras and lay between Laurentia to the north-west and Avalonia-Baltica to the south-east. It closed as these continents collided during the Caledonian Orogeny.
Panthalassic Ocean	The superocean that surrounded Pangaea, the name means 'entire sea'.
North Sea	This sea came into existence as an offshoot of the Atlantic Ocean and today it separates Britain from Europe and Scandanavia.
Rheic Ocean	The ocean that opened up between Gondwana to the south and Avalonia as it drifted northwards.
Tethys Ocean	The ocean that opened up between Gondwana and Laurasia as Pangaea broke apart. As the Atlantic Ocean came into existence the Tethys began to close.
Zechstein Sea	An inland sea that existed across an area that correlates with today's North Sea and lowland parts of Britain and northern Europe during the Permian period.

Rock Data

Rock	Type	Characteristics
Agglomerate	Igneous (extrusive/volcanic)	Pyroclastic volcanic material that contains large volcanic bombs and other rock fragments.
Andesite	Igneous (extrusive/volcanic)	An intermediate volcanic rock that is somewhere between runny basaltic and viscous rhyolitic magma. It can be fine-grained or feature large crystals. Named after the Andes mountains in South America.
Basalt	Igneous (extrusive/volcanic)	Formed from fast-flowing runny lava that issues from volcanoes or fissures in the sea bed. It is the most commonly occuring rock in the oceanic crust and is rich in magnesium and iron. It is usually black and is chemically equivalent to plutonic gabbro and dolerite.
Calcite (mineral)		A crystaline form of calcium carbonate. Veins form in host rocks where calcium carbonate dissolved in solution seeps into cracks and then evaporates to leave crystals. It also commonly occurs as a cement holding sedimentary rocks together.
Chalk	Sedimentary	An exceptionally fine and pure variety of white limestone formed from coccolithophores, a type of microscopic algae comprised of calcium carbonate plates that have settled on the sea bed.
Chert	Sedimentary	A fine-grained silica-rich rock that is a common component of shingle. The colour varies but it is commonly grey, brown, red, pink or off-white, and is slightly translucent.
Coal	Sedimentary	Rock that is formed out of compressed peat layers, which are the remains of decomposed vegetable matter.
Conglomerate	Sedimentary	Formed from rounded fragments of other rocks. Often associated with sandstone where the fragments are cemented together with smaller particles of quartz.
Dolomite or dolostone	Sedimentary	Dolomite, or magnesian limestone, is a limestone where the calcium carbonate has been partially replaced by magnesium carbonate. Usually a pale rock, sometimes gold in colour.
Dolerite	Igneous (intrusive/plutonic)	A subvolcanic rock that never reaches the surface although it pushes up through gaps in other rocks to create dykes and sills. It is equivalent to volcanic basalt or plutonic gabbro.
Felsite	Igneous (intrusive/plutonic)	A plutonic rock composed primarily of feldspar and quartz.
Flint	Sedimentary	A type of chert that is formed form the remains of silcaceous sea sponges. Usually grey or black and found in the form of nodules, sometimes seams, which are frequently uncovered in chalk beds.
Gabbro	Igneous (intrusive/plutonic)	A large group of dark, coarse-grained rocks that are chemically equivalent to basalt although they are formed in plutons underneath the Earth's crust and are later revealed by erosion.
Gneiss	Metamorphic	Formed by high-grade metamorphic processes working on existing igneous or sedimentary rocks. Tends to foliated (layered) as component crystals are resorted during the transformation. These are some of the oldest rocks on the planet and much of it dates from the Precambrian.
Granite	Igneous (intrusive/plutonic)	Silica and aluminium rich granite forms in plutons and because the rock cools slowly underground the crystals reach a large size that are clearly visible to the naked eye. Most granites are formed from three silicate minerals: quartz, mica and feldspar. Can be pink, orange, grey or white, dependent on which minerals are present.
Halite or rock salt (mineral)		A crystaline form of sodium chloride, i.e. table salt, that is created when oceans or saline lake waters evaporate to leave salt pans.
Ironstone	Sedimentary	A sandstone that is rich in iron, often occurring as nodules among other sedimentary rocks.

Limestone	Sedimentary	Primarily created from the calcium carbonate rich remains of hard-shelled marine organisms, including coral reefs, that have settled on the seabed. It also comes in an oolitic form where tiny spherical concretions form around a nucleus, such as a sand grain, and these are also largely calcium carbonate. Can be grey, off-white and sometimes pale gold.
Mudstone	Sedimentary	A fine grained rock similar to siltstone that is composed of mud made up of clay and silt particles.
Phyllite	Metamorphic	Derived from an original shale-type rock that has already been metamorphosed into slate and then transformed further still due to another episode of/or continued exposure to heat and pressure.
Porphyry	Igneous (intrusive/plutonic)	A type of rock that has substantially large crystals suspended within a fine grained matrix. The term is is always prefixed by a rock type i.e. quartz porphyry to indicate the composition.
Pumice	Igneous (extrusive/volcanic)	A light-grey rock with a pitted-texture formed from frothy lava where the gas contained therein creates bubbles (vesicles) that remain as the rock cools. Known for being able to float on water.
Quartzite	Metamorphic	A pale grey-coloured rock that is derived from sandstone that is high in quartz and low in other sediments. Metamorphosed due to the pressure associated with tectonic events into a rock harder than the original sandstone.
Rhyolite	Igneous (extrusive/volcanic)	Composed of the same minerals as granite although the crystals are too small to be seen with the naked eye. Because it is silica-rich it forms a viscous lava that is prone to erupting violently and is associated with pyroclastic flows. The clouds of ash and other ejecta from these events solidify into a rock type known as tuff.
Sandstone	Sedimentary	Formed from sand-sized grains that are frequently quartz or sometimes feldspar. Can form in deserts, rivers, deltas and oceans, and is ubiquitous. Comes in many forms such as greywacke, gritstone and old red sandstone, to name just a few, and various colours.
Schist	Metamorphic	An intermediate metamorphic rock commonly derived from shales and slates, although it can be of an igneous origin. Many schists are mica based, which creates a natural sparkle, however some feature graphite (carbon) and chlorites.
Scoria	Igneous (extrusive/volcanic)	A dark-coloured rock with vesicles that shares similarities with pumice, however being rich in iron it is much heavier and does not float.
Serpentinite or serpentine	Metamorphic	Composed of one or more of the serpentine group of minerals. These rocks are more usually seen at plate boundaries on the sea floor, however they occasionally become detached and embedded into continental crust. They are among the most variable and deformed rocks seen on land.
Shale	Sedimentary	A fine-grained rock composed of mud that is a mix of flakes of clay minerals and silt-sized particles of other minerals, especially quartz and calcite It is recognisable due to its fissile nature, meaning that it splits readily along the bedding plane.
Silica (mineral)		Frequently takes the form of feldspar and quartz, which are the first and second most abundant minerals in the Earth's crust respectively, and are both common ingredients of sand. Silica is a primary constiuent of both granite and sandstone among other rocks. It can form mineral veins in host rocks in the same manner as calcite.
Siltstone	Sedimentary	A very fine grained sedimentary rock similar to mudstone but composed primarily of silt rather than clay particles.
Slate	Metamorphic	A fine-grained rock derived from an original shale-type rock that has been transformed by low-grade metamorphism. Slate has a laminated structure that means it is easily split into thin sheets, hence its use as roof tiles.

Photographic Information

Half title page: Torridon across the Sound of Raasay 200mm, 2 secs, f/18, ISO 100, Canon 5D

Title page: Elegug Stacks 20mm, ½–⅛ secs (two exposures combined), f/16, ISO 100, Canon 5D mk ii

Contents page: Borthwen and Lleyn Peninsula peaks 70mm, 8–20 secs (two exposures stitched together), f/22, ISO 100, Canon 5D

1 Taigh Bhurigh and Toe Head 17mm, 1.3–⅓ sec (two exposures combined), f/22, ISO 100, Canon 5D

2 Rubha na Griosaich 17mm, ⅛ sec, f/16, ISO 100, Canon 5D, polarising filter

3 Ben Wyvis 70mm, 1/13 sec (three exposures stitched together), f/18, ISO 200, Canon 5D mk II, polarising filter

4 Beinn Eighe 17mm, 1/13 sec, f/18, ISO 100, Canon 5D, polarising filter

5 Liathach 21mm, 1/10–1/200 sec (three exposures combined), f/16, ISO 200, Canon 5D mk II, polarising filter

6 Stac Pollaidh 21mm, 0.6 sec, f/18, ISO 100, Canon 5D mk II, polarising filter

7 Bow Fiddle Rock 23mm, 2.0–½ sec (two exposures combined), f/14, ISO 100, Canon 5D mk II

8 The Cobbler (Ben Arthur) 27mm, 1/13 sec, f/16, ISO 200, Canon 5D mk II, polarising filter

9 Twelve Pins of Connemara 24mm (tilt & shift), ⅓–⅕ sec (four exposures stitched together), f/16, ISO 100, Canon 5D mk II

10 Paps of Jura 70mm, 1/125–1/800 sec (various exposures combined and stitched together), f/11, ISO 200, Canon 5D mk II

11 Llanddwyn Island 17mm, ⅕ sec, f/18, ISO 100, Canon 5D mk II

12 Bwa Gwyn 17mm, 3.2–1.6 sec (two exposures combined), f/18, ISO 100, Canon 5D mk II

13 Malvern Hills 38mm, 1.6–1.3 sec (two exposures combined), f/16, ISO 100, Canon 5D mk II, polarising filter used

14 Long Mynd & the Wrekin 135mm, 0.6 sec, f/16, ISO 200, Canon 5D mk II

15 Smoo Cave 37mm, 50.0 secs, f/16, ISO 100, Canon 5D mk II

16 The Rhinogydd 27mm, ⅛ sec, f/16, ISO 100, Canon 5D mk II, polarising filter

17 Doldrum Bay 26mm, 1.3–½ sec (two exposures combined), f/16, ISO 100, Canon 5D mk II

18 Schiehallion 35mm, ¼ sec, f/16, ISO 100, Canon 5D mk II, polarising filter

19 Rhobell Fawr 28mm, 1/13 sec, f/16, ISO 200, Canon 5D mk II

20 Skiddaw 17mm, ⅛–1/15 sec (two exposures combined), f/16, ISO 200, Canon 5D mk II

21 Devil's Chair, Stiperstones 17mm, ⅓–1/15 sec (two exposures combined), f/16, ISO 200, Canon 5D mk II, polarising filter

22 St David's Head 23mm, ⅙–1/13 sec (two exposures combined), f/16, ISO 200, Canon 5D mk II

23 Carn Menyn 22mm, ⅓ sec, f/16, ISO 200, Canon 5D mk II, polarising filter

24 Pen Anglas 19mm, 0.8 sec, f/16, ISO 100, Canon 5D mk II

25 Mweelrea and Killary Harbour 20mm, ⅛–1/15 sec (two exposures combined), f/11, ISO 100, Canon 5D mk II, polarising filter

26 Cadair Idris 17mm, 5.0–2.0 sec (various exposures combined and stitched), f/16, ISO 100, Canon 5D, polarising filter

27 Glyder Fach 19mm, ⅓ sec, f/22, ISO 100, Canon 5D, polarising filter

28 Snowdon 17mm, 0.9 sec, f/16, ISO 100, Canon 5D mk II, polarising filter

29 Helvellyn 17mm, ½ sec, f/16, ISO 100, Canon 5D mk II, polarising filter

30 Great Gable 94mm, ⅕ sec, f/16, ISO 100, Canon 5D mk II

31 Wastwater 20mm, ⅕–1/20 sec (two exposures combined), f/16, ISO 200, Canon 5D mk II

32 Howgill Fells 22mm, 1.0 sec, f/20, ISO 200, Canon 5D mk II, polarising filter

33 Grey Man of Merrick 28mm, ⅙ sec, f/16, ISO 100, Canon 5D mk II, polarising filter

34 Constitution Hill/Craig-glais 19mm, 0.8–⅓ sec (two exposures combined), f/16, ISO 100, Canon 5D mk II, polarising filter

35 Croagh Patrick 20mm, ⅓–1/15 sec (two exposures combined), f/16, ISO 100, Canon 5D mk II

36 Wenlock Edge 78mm, ½–⅙ sec (four exposures stitched together), f/11, ISO 100, Canon 5D mk II, polarising filter

37 Clogher Head 26mm, ½–⅛ sec (two exposures combined), f/16, ISO 100, Canon 5D mk II, polarising filter

38 Siccar Point 25mm, 0.6–¼ sec (two exposures combined), f/16, ISO 100, Canon 5D mk II, polarising filter

39 Kintra 145mm, 0.8 sec, f/32, ISO 100, Canon 5D mk II, polarising filter

40 The Three Sisters 27mm, 1/30 sec, f/16, ISO 200, Canon 5D mk II

41 Buachaille Etive Mor 23mm, ½–⅕ sec (two exposures combined), f/16, ISO 100, Canon 5D mk II, polarising filter

42 Ben Nevis 27mm, 1.6–0.8 sec (two exposures combined), f/16, ISO 100, Canon 5D mk II, polarising filter

43 Devil's Point 21mm, 0.6 sec, f/18, ISO 50, Canon 5D mk II

44 The Cheviot 36mm, 1.3 secs, f/22, ISO 200, Canon 5D mk II

45 Pen y Fan 21mm, ⅙–1/30 sec (two exposures combined), f/16, ISO 100, Canon 5D mk II, polarising filter

46 Sugar Loaf 29mm, ⅛–1/15 sec (two exposures combined), f/18, ISO 200, Canon 5D mk II, polarising filter

47 Carrauntoohil & Hag's Tooth 75mm, ⅓ sec (four exposures stitched together), f/8, ISO 100, Canon 5D mk II

48 Old Man of Hoy 34mm, ⅛–1/20 sec (two exposures combined), f/16, ISO 100, Canon 5D mk II

49 The Lizard/Kynance Cove 27mm, 5.0 secs, f/22, ISO 100, Canon 5D mk II

50 Bedruthan Steps 21mm, ½–⅛ sec (three exposures combined), f/18, ISO 200, Canon 5D

51 Arthur's Seat/Salisbury Crags 19mm, 2.0–1.0 secs (two exposures combined), f/16, ISO 100, Canon 5D mk II, polarising filter

52 Eildon Hills 30mm, ⅓–⅙ sec (two exposures combined), f/18, ISO 100, Canon 5D mk II, polarising filter

53 Mewslade Bay 30mm, 1.3–0.8 secs (two exposures combined), f/18, ISO 100, Canon 5D mk II

54 Winnats Pass 17mm, 1/15 sec, f/16, ISO 100, Canon 5D mk II, polarising filter

55 Cheddar Gorge 29mm, 1/8 sec, f/13, ISO 200, Canon 5D mk II

56 Ben Bulben 87mm, 0.6–1/4 sec (four exposures stitched together), f/22, ISO 100, Canon 5D mk II, polarising filter

57 Malham Cove 25mm, 0.6 sec, f/22, ISO 100, Canon 5D mk II, polarising filter

58 The Burren 30mm, 1/13 sec, f/16, ISO 200, Canon 5D mk II

59 Twisleton Scars & Whernside 40mm, 0.6 sec, f/22, ISO 100, Canon 5D, polarising filter

60 Stanage Edge 25mm, 1/10 sec, f/16, ISO 250, Canon 5D mk II, polarising filter

61 Cliffs of Moher 20mm, 0.8 sec, f/16, ISO 200, Canon 5D mk II, polarising filter

62 Alport Castles 20mm, 1/4 sec, f/16, ISO 100, Canon 5D mk II, polarising filter

63 Brimham Rocks 22mm, 1/4 sec, f/18, ISO 200, Canon 5D mk II, polarising filter

64 Millook Haven 30mm, 1/2 sec, f/16, ISO 100, Canon 5D mk II, polarising filter

65 Haytor 30mm, 1/3–1/8 sec (two exposures combined), f/16, ISO 200, Canon 5D mk II

66 Cheesewring Tor 17mm, 1/5–1/10 sec (two exposures combined), f/16, ISO 200, Canon 5D mk II, polarising filter

67 Bamburgh/Harkess Rocks 30mm, 15.0 secs, f/18, ISO 100, Canon 5D

68 High Cup Nick 21mm, 1/15–1/30 sec (two exposures combined), f/16, ISO 100, Canon 5D mk II

69 Merkland Point 40mm, 0.8–1/2 sec (two exposures combined), f/22, ISO 100, Canon 5D mk II, polarising filter

70 Langstone Rock 17mm, 1/5–1/8 sec (two exposures combined), f/16, ISO 100, Canon 5D mk II, polarising filter

71 Lot's Wife 24mm (tilt & shift), 1/6 sec, f/11, ISO 100, Canon 5D mk II, polarising filter

72 Ladram Bay 19mm, 10.0–4.0 secs (two exposures combined), f/16, ISO 100, Canon 5D

73 Kinver Edge 29mm, 1/2 sec, f/16, ISO 100, Canon 5D mk II

74 Nash Point 17mm, 5.0 secs, f/18, ISO 100, Canon 5D

75 Kilve 19mm, 10.0 secs, f/18, ISO 100, Canon 5D

76 Elgol 17mm, 0.8 sec, f/22, ISO 100, Canon 5D

77 Durdle Door 40mm, 1/10–1/25 sec (two exposures combined), f/16, ISO 100, Canon 5D mk II

78 Black Nab 21mm, 1/4 sec, f/16, ISO 100, Canon 5D, polarising filter

79 Roseberry Topping 29mm, 1/4 sec, f/18, ISO 100, Canon 5D, polarising filter

80 Golden Cap 23mm, 1/4–1/10 sec (two exposures combined), f/18, ISO 100, Canon 5D mk II

81 Thornwick Nab 17mm, 1/5 sec, f/16, ISO 100, Canon 5D mk II, polarising filter

82 Devil's Dyke 30mm, 1/15 sec, f/18, ISO 250, Canon 5D mk II, polarising filter

83 White Cliffs of Dover 17mm, 13.0 secs, f/16, ISO 100, Canon 5D mk II, polarising filter

84 Hunstanton Cliff 40mm, 1/4 sec, f/16, ISO 100, Canon 5D mk II, polarising filter

85 Whiterocks Beach 19mm, 1/4 sec, f/11, ISO 100, Canon 5D mk II, polarising filter

86 Carrick-a-Rede 22mm, 1.3–1/3 secs (two exposures combined), f/22, ISO 100, Canon 5D mk II

87 Giant's Causeway 24mm (tilt & shift), 1/5–1/25 secs (two exposures combined), f/16, ISO 200, Canon 5D mk II

88 Fingal's Cave 24mm (tilt & shift), 1/4 sec, f/16, ISO 100, Canon 5D mk II

89 Binevenagh 29mm, 1/2 sec, f/16, ISO 200, Canon 5D mk II, polarising filter

90 The Storr 70mm, 1.6 sec, f/18, ISO 100, Canon 5D, polarising filter

91 The Quiraing 17mm, 1.3–1/3 sec (two exposures combined), f/16, ISO 100, Canon 5D mk II

92 Cuillin 70mm, 2.0 sec (three exposures stitched together) f/22, ISO 100, Canon 5D

93 Rum Cuillin 32mm, 1/5–1/13 sec (two exposures combined), f/18, ISO 100, Canon 5D mk II

94 Caisteal Abhail 19mm, 1/6–1/100 sec (three exposures combined), f/18, ISO 200, Canon 5D mk II

95 Slieve Binnian 22mm, 1/13 sec, f/14, ISO 250, Canon 5D mk II, polarising filter

96 Alum Bay 28mm, 1/8 sec, f/16, ISO 100, Canon 5D mk II, polarising filter

97 Hengistbury Head 22mm, 1/3 sec, f/18, ISO 100, Canon 5D mk II, polarising filter

98 Clew Bay 75mm, 1/5–1/25 sec (various exposures combined and stitched), f/8, ISO 200, Canon 5D mk II, polarising filter

99 Chesil Beach 84mm, 120 sec (two exposures stitched together) f/22, ISO 100, Canon 5D mk II

100 Sands of Forvie 17mm, 1/3 sec, f/16, ISO 100, Canon 5D mk II, polarising filter

DETAIL PHOTOGRAPHS (PAGES 10–14)

Portknockie, Moray, banded quartzite 40mm, 1/2 sec, f/18, ISO 100, Canon 5D mk II, polarising filter

Gable Beck, Wasdale, pink granite 25mm, 2.0 sec, f/18, ISO 200, Canon 5D mk II

St David's Head, Pembrokeshire, oxidised gabbro 40mm, 1/4 sec, f/22, ISO 200, Canon 5D mk II, polarising filter

Pease Bay, Berwickshire, Old Red Sandstone 40mm, 3.2 sec, f/22, ISO 100, Canon 5D mk II

The Burren, County Clare, limestone pavement 40mm, 1/3 sec, f/18, ISO 200, Canon 5D mk II

Millook Haven, Cornwall, quartz in killas 87mm, 2.5 secs, f/22, ISO 100, Canon 5D mk II,polarising filter

Holy Island, Northumberland, dolerite 40mm, 1.0 sec, f/18, ISO 1200, Canon 5D, polarising filter

Littleham Cove, Devon, radioactive ore in mudstone 40mm, 1/6 sec, f/22, ISO 100, Canon 5D mk II, polarising filter

Lyme Regis, Dorset, limestone 29mm, 1/6 sec, f/11, ISO 100, Canon 5D mk II, polarising filter

Elgol, Isle of Skye, sandstone 40mm, 1/2 sec, f/22, ISO 100, Canon 5D

White Rocks Bay, County Antrim, flint in chalk 40mm, 1/15 sec, f/22, ISO 100, Canon 5D mk II

Cleiteadh nan Sgarbh, Arran, quartz-porphyry and granite 40mm, 1/2 sec, f/22, ISO 100, Canon 5D mk II, polarising filter